GROWING GREENER CITIES

A TREE-PLANTING HANDBOOK

GLOBAL RELEAF

by
Gary Moll & Stanley Young

Illustrated by
Thomas C. Whittemore

LIVING PLANET
P R E S S
LOS ANGELES

Published in the United States by Living Planet Press
558 Rose Avenue, Venice, California 90291

Distributed by Publishers Group West, Emeryville, California

Interior design and page layout: Karen Bowers
Cover design: Annmarie Dalton

**Discounts for bulk orders are available from the publisher.
Call (310) 396-0188.**

ISBN 1-879326-13-2

 Printed on recycled paper

Manufactured in the United States of America

Library of Congress catalog card number 91-78089

10 9 8 7 6 5 4 3 2 1

CONTENTS

PART III: GLOBAL RELEAF, THE COMMUNITY, AND THE WORLD

FOREWORD

 My musical career has given me the opportunity to travel the world and to experience firsthand the importance of the individual in implementing change. We all have a voice in our future, and a choice in the actions we take. Everything we do, from brushing our teeth to starting our cars, affects the environment for better or for worse. As the world population moves toward 6 billion people, our environmental impact is growing more potent each year. This impact is nowhere more evident than in our cities. When people congregate in ever greater numbers, the negative consequences are formidable. Living in Southern California, I have witnessed years of polluted air and water. We may not be able to clean up our cities overnight, but we can start to make a difference by making them greener places. Planting a tree may be the simplest, most immediate, and most effective way to make a personal commitment to the environment.

Growing Greener Cities will inform you about trees and the critical role they play in the natural cycles of the Earth. You will learn why we should plant more trees and take better care of the ones we have—and then find out how to do it step by step. This book is for people who want to add their voices to mine, to Global ReLeaf, and to the millions of individuals who are taking positive actions to help the environment.

Ecology is the study of balance. Proper balance creates harmony. If we can learn to "harmonize," we can create a voice more powerful than the sum of its parts and help to change the way we think about the environment. So plant a tree in your yard, join with a community group to plant and care for the trees in your neighborhood, let your local leaders know that you care about the trees along the streets and in the parks, and help them learn more about the ecological benefits trees provide. We not only have the responsibility but the power to make our planet a greener and healthier place.

—Graham Nash

ACKNOWLEDGMENTS

This book represents the ideals of the American Forestry Association (AFA) in every sense of the word. Staff members are involved in detailed conservation work every day, ranging from policy work on Capitol Hill to digging holes to plant trees with local tree groups. The staff of the American Forestry Association deserves a thank-you for their help, along with two AFA board members, Bob Skiera and Donald Willeke.

A few people at AFA deserve special recognition for the major roles they played in getting this book to press. Deborah Gangloff, vice president of program services, is our Global ReLeaf expert. She gave me guidance and support from the early development of the book to production. Dan Smith, director of communications, was an excellent reviewer, partner, and promoter; and Neil Sampson, our executive vice president, encouraged us to do the book and helped write about the tough issues, such as hydrocarbons. Lastly, thanks to my wife, Diane, who reminds me to keep life in perspective.

— G.M.

Thanks to Dinah Berland at Living Planet Press for her constant grace and expertise under pressure; to Stephen Tukel and Joshua Horwitz for letting me branch out; and as ever, to Janice for her understanding, and now Alyssa, who will enjoy tomorrow's shade of our flourishing urban forests.

— S.Y.

PART I:

WELCOME TO THE URBAN FOREST

A FOREST GROWS IN THE CITY

Look around. You may not realize it, but you are living in the midst of a forest. Every tree you see is linked to all the other trees and plants throughout the city. This delicate network is a living system that contributes to the well-being of our environment, cleansing and cooling the air, shading our streets and beautifying the world we inhabit. We call this living, growing system "the urban forest," a wondrous web of life and a crucial element in the health and livability of our cities. As we head into the twenty-first century, the role that trees play in our cities will become increasingly important.

The term *urban forest* may be new to you. Perhaps you find the word "forest" to be something of an exaggeration, especially when you consider the mostly treeless state of your inner city. But the use of "forest" is no exaggeration, for it refers to the city as a whole and helps us to see it that way—trees, buildings, people,

everything. While Manhattan, or Tucson, or downtown Los Angeles may not resemble the sylvan spots you remember from camping trips, each one is, in fact, as much a living system as the densest reaches of a verdant national park.

A Thread of Life

Were you to hover over your own city, you would see that about one-third of the urban area is covered by a canopy of trees. Another third of the typical American city is covered by grass and other vegetation; the rest is streets and structures. Beneath the canopy—the trees' upper area—is a dense, living network of leaves and twigs with a collective surface area that is four times as large as the total surface area of the city's buildings, roads, and sidewalks. The city, far from being a barren and unnatural intrusion into the world, is in fact mostly a "living landscape," a true ecosystem. And it operates in much the same way as a rural forest: pumping water from the ground, exchanging gases, modifying airflow, and cleansing the atmosphere.

The Need for Trees

The urban forest is important to the well-being of our cities for a multitude of reasons. Perhaps the most overlooked is the simplest and the most powerful: we like trees. We enjoy being in their company; we value their shade and their beauty. A city landscape without trees is likely to feel barren, lifeless, and inhospitable. Trees carry with them the most basic elements of life; they fulfill needs that are ancient and deep.

"I saw a glade," writes author Jean Liedloff of a childhood experience she had one summer in Maine. "It had a lush fir tree at the far side and a knoll in the center covered in bright, almost luminous green moss. I felt the anxiety that colored my life fall away. Everything was in its place—the tree, the earth underneath, the rock, the moss. I felt I had discovered the missing center of things . . ."

There is indeed a magic to trees. Rooted in the earth, their branches stretching toward the heavens, they are a living link between the realms of our life. They shade and shelter. They give us a feeling of security and make us feel at home. And no wonder—according to Darwin, the green canopy above us was once our original "living room" before we descended from the branches to walk upright on the ground. Trees were our first habitat, and in their presence we feel protected and at home.

There is also something grand about trees. Their age and stature lend our surroundings a quiet nobility. The presence of these lofty beings enhances our lives and provides visual relief from the square walls of our dwellings and the containment of our workplaces.

MAKING THE CITY LIVABLE

It is no coincidence that the cities rated "most livable" always have an abundance of trees. Most of these cities recognize the crucial role that trees play in terms of enhancing the urban environment and have turned their commitment into law. Local ordinances assure urban forests a secure future and give them an important place in each city's infrastructure and funding.

Milwaukee, as one example, has a separate forestry division within its department of public works. It also maintains a wide-ranging street-tree program, and involves thousands of people in an Arbor Day program with the visible participation of the mayor and city aldermen. Minneapolis cherishes its tree-lined streets, and the city spent millions of dollars in a successful program to save 86,000 of its elms while that species was being ravaged elsewhere by disease. Other cities, such as Charlotte, North Carolina; Evanston, Illinois; and Austin, Texas, all have continuing commitments to their urban forests, a clear indication of their vibrant sense of pride and identity.

Urban Forests: Stretched to the Breaking Point

Today, sadly, many other cities are cutting back on their tree programs, even though the need to support the planting and care of our urban forests nationally has never been more pressing or more important.

In many cities, the thin thread of life that is the urban forest is stretched to the breaking point. Yes, there is a forest about us, but it is not a forest simply because we find two trees on the same street;

Trees, Myths, and Paradise

"The groves were God's first temples," wrote William Cullen Bryant, the American poet. Trees have always inspired us and captured our imagination. The Bible relates the tale of the Garden of Eden, with its Tree of Knowledge and Tree of Life. Hindu mythology tells of the great primal forest and its central tree, the mighty Jambu, which bore fruit as large as an elephant and from whose seeds flowed the purest gold. In Asia, the Buddha achieved enlightenment under the Bo tree, whose leaves are still considered a symbol of spirituality. Samoans believed that a coconut tree grew near the entrance to Pulotu, the World of Spirits. Should a wandering spirit strike the tree, it would have to return to the body for another lifetime of earthly existence. In Norse mythology, Ygdrasill, an evergreen ash tree, held the universe together, its roots in the underworld and its branches extended into the heavenly realms of the sky. The Greeks and Romans felt that the human race was the fruit of trees. "These woods," wrote the poet Virgil, "were first the seat of sylvan power and savage men who took their birth from the trunks of trees and stubborn oaks."

Often a particular type of tree was thought to have magical powers. Ancient Danes believed that the good mother of elves—the Elder Queen—lived in the roots of the elder tree. Before removing a branch or cutting down an elder, it was necessary to ask permission of the Elder Queen herself to prevent misfortune. In Russia, the elder tree was used to keep evil spirits out of houses. And in England, the elder was often found growing beside country cottages to keep evil at bay. (An elder twig in the pocket was also said to cure rheumatism.)

Other trees served equally well as guardians against the forces of darkness. "Witches have no power where there is rowan-tree wood," goes one English madrigal concerning the red-berried rowan, or European mountain ash. Many a person would place a rowan branch under his or her bed to keep witches away; a small cross made from the rowan's branches placed in the churn protected butter and cheese from the evil influence of errant sorceresses.

French Canadians believed that Jack Pine, a spirit with evil and capricious powers, dwelt in the stump and roots of the pine tree. Rather than cut it out to remove it, they would pile brush around it and burn it.

Many Native Americans believed tall trees were the homes of spirits who cried out when the trees were cut down. Members of the Hidatsa tribe in the upper Missouri Valley felt that the cottonwood tree had an intelligence of its own and would come to the aid of individuals if beckoned. Tribal elders held that the irresponsible cutting of sacred cottonwoods in the last century led directly to the Hidatsas' later misfortunes.

Germans and Slavs often planted a tree in front of a newlywed couple's house. Many families in Europe would plant a tree upon the birth of a baby, especially an heir, whose fate was then tied up with that of the tree's.

Trees were used to help fortune tellers to divine the meaning of dreams. In medieval Europe, dreaming of a green oak tree indicated a long life; a cypress was the harbinger of problems in business. Dreaming of a palm tree was the best of omens, while the vision of a pine was a dark hint of looming problems.

the healthy urban forest, like a rural forest, needs diversity, large numbers of trees, and proper conditions for continued growth.

In the past, a society counted its wealth in terms of its cultural heritage and the health of its trade and economy. Today, we must add a determinant of national pride: biological diversity, a living heritage. How do we deal with our natural patrimony, with species that have been here for eons, old-growth forests that are irreplaceable? The urban forest is a more recent but vital part of our biological inheritance—a gift and resource to be cherished and nurtured.

GLOBAL WARMING

The importance of the urban forest extends well beyond the metropolitan or even national boundaries. The condition of our urban forests now has global environmental implications. Eight of the hottest years of the century occurred during the 1980s and early 1990s. Is this a harbinger of a large-scale upward shift in global temperatures, or only a statistical blip that doesn't signify any major change? Not all the evidence is in, but there are clear indications that something is seriously amiss. "Global climate and chemical cycles have undergone dramatic and closely linked changes," say the authors of the September 1989 issue of *Scientific American*. Extensive smog and air pollution, acid rain, and depletion of the ozone layer are the direct results of industrial and other emissions, and they are all linked to the possibility of major global climate changes in the coming century.

The Earth has gone through cycles of temperature changes before. At the end of the Pleistocene epoch, 10,000 years ago, the Earth's temperature rose by 10 degrees Fahrenheit over a 1,000-year period. In contrast, scientists now estimate that the current predicted rise in temperature—between 5 and 9 degrees Fahrenheit by the middle of the next century—is more rapid and potentially disastrous. This much warming would cause some of the Earth's ice caps to melt, resulting in higher ocean levels and widespread flooding of low-lying areas such as Bangladesh and Florida. Worldwide weather patterns would

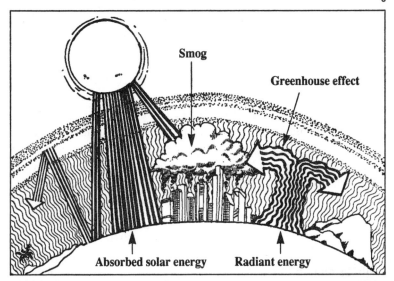

Smog

Greenhouse effect

Absorbed solar energy   **Radiant energy**

The greenhouse effect is produced when the increase of carbon dioxide and certain other gases in the air traps the sun's energy near the surface of the Earth, causing an increase in the temperature of the atmosphere.

change, resulting in droughts in the American Midwest, and increased monsoon conditions in India. An expert at the Smithsonian Institution estimates that 15 percent of all species alive today could become extinct as the changing weather patterns remove or alter their habitats.

Fighting the Greenhouse Effect

Global warming is the potential result of a phenomenon known as the *greenhouse effect*. The Earth's atmosphere functions much like the glass of a greenhouse. Much of the sunlight that reaches our planet is reflected back to space by the upper reaches of the atmosphere, but a small amount, in the form of short-wave energy, is able to slice its way through the 7-mile-high barrier of atmospheric gases. After hitting the Earth's surface, it is reflected back as long-wave radiation. This energy then becomes radiant (or heat) energy, some of which is reflected back into the atmosphere where it remains trapped, a process that has kept the temperature of the Earth stable for hundreds of millions of years.

Since the Industrial Revolution, the amounts and types of these greenhouse gases, mostly methane and especially carbon dioxide, have increased. The burning of fossil fuels and the wholesale cutting of forest areas have driven the amount of carbon dioxide in the air from 280 parts per million (ppm) in the year 1800 to its present-day 350 ppm—a 7 percent increase per century. This rise in carbon dioxide and the infusion of other chemicals, such as chlorofluorocarbons (CFCs) produced by industries, have conspired to make the Earth's atmosphere more efficient at trapping the sun's reflected heat. And, like an increasingly efficient greenhouse, the Earth's atmosphere is driving up the surface temperatures of the planet.

Ecology and Carbon

Ecology is the science that explains the interaction of living things with the Earth's natural chemistry at a scale we can see, touch, and observe. The "web of life" is an analogy often used to explain this interdependence of one living thing on another. The importance of carbon in this process cannot be overstated; it is the single most important element on Earth. Essentially, every living thing is built on a carbon frame with various combinations of hydrogen, oxygen, nitrogen, and traces of other elements attached to it.

Trees are an integral part of the ecological web of life and play an ever-present role in the life cycles of the Earth. Because they are the largest vascular plants on Earth, they work like a master conductor in orchestrating the growth and development of an ecosystem.

Large tree canopies capture huge amounts of sunlight which fuel photosynthesis and plant growth. In addition, trees soak up carbon from the air and soil, and store it in their trunks, branches, and roots. Trees are always products of the environment and a living measure of the quality of life. In the arrangement of living things, their grandeur might be compared to the great cathedrals, such as Notre Dame, built by European masons. Given the right conditions, trees produce giant pillars and an arching canopy of leaves. This abundance of leaves and branches has an effect on the local chemistry and modifies the environment, improving ecological conditions for a wide range of other living things.

Trees and Carbon Dioxide

Of the eight greenhouse gases, carbon dioxide (CO_2) is the most abundant, constituting over half of the total heat-trapping gases in the atmosphere. The planetary counterbalance to this build-up of carbon dioxide has been the oceans, which absorb the gas; and the trees and forests of the planet, which "fix" carbon dioxide into their structure during photosynthesis. Ninety percent of the carbon that is fixed in solid form on the Earth's surface is held in the world's forests.

Trees are an integral part of any plan to reverse the potentially devastating rise in global temperatures, and the urban forest plays as critical a role in the reduction of carbon dioxide in the atmosphere as do the massive forests of the Amazon—simply because the urban forest affects human use of energy resources.

In a rural forest, each tree takes in atmospheric carbon dioxide at the rate of 26 pounds a year and releases about 13 pounds of oxygen—enough oxygen throughout the day to keep a family of four breathing. In the city, there are fewer trees per acre, but each tree plays a powerful role in the carbon equation. An urban tree lowers the temperature in summer and raises it in winter. The result is that we use less energy to make ourselves comfortable, which saves energy and prevents CO_2 production. When you take a tree's ability to store carbon and add it to the tree's energy-saving potential, an urban tree has up to fifteen times the benefit of its rural cousin.

JANITORS OF THE AIR

Not only do trees remove carbon dioxide from the atmosphere, but recent studies show that they also filter "particulate matter" (microscopic dust particles) and remove some toxic pollutants as well. In particular, trees have been shown to "capture" a wide range of chemical compounds in the air that are produced by fuel combustion and other processes, and which have been shown to be smog-producing and dangerous to our health.

A Windfall from Trees

Trees are on the job 24 hours a day, 365 days a year. Just how much is their unceasing effort worth? The American Forestry Association did a recent study and came up with the following figures, indicating the dollar value of an urban tree with a fifty-year life span. A single tree would provide this much dollar-value benefit for one year:

>Air conditioning : $73
>Controlling erosion and storm water: $75
>Wildlife shelter: $75
>Controlling air pollution: $50

The total is $273 a year. Compounding this amount for fifty years at 5 percent, the grand total is $57,151.

Hard Cash: Real Estate, Trees, and Lot Values

Urban trees are worth much more than the value of their wood—twenty-five times more than their country cousins in the forest—since city trees enhance the value of real estate. In some cases, trees can raise the value of a lot compared to the same lot without trees by as much as 20 percent. On average, trees add between 5 and 7 percent to the value of a house lot. Nationwide, that added value results in an extra $5,000 per lot, according the U.S. Forest Service. And a piece of property with trees invariably sells faster, too.

How Much Are My Trees Worth?

The best way to determine the value of the trees on your property is to find out the cost of the retail replacement of similar sized trees at your local nursery. Make sure the quote includes planting and a one-year guarantee.

Tree experts sometimes use a formula method of estimating a tree's value based on its size and other factors. This method is especially useful for trees that are too mature to compare with nursery stock. First, determine an average base value by measuring the diameter of the tree's trunk 4-1/2 feet from the ground. Here are some average base values of trees of various sizes:

Diameter of trunk at 4-1/2 feet	Average base value
10"	$ 1,729
14"	$ 3,388
26"	$11,682
30"	$15,554

Adjust this figure according to the species, location, and condition of your tree:

• **Species Value:** 100 percent for the best types of trees in your area; 70 percent for less desirable species.
• **Location:** 100 percent for a yard tree; 90 percent for a tree 15 to 20 feet from the corner of the house; 70 percent or less for one that is too close to the sidewalk, or directly in front of a picture window.
• **Condition:** The health of your tree will obviously influence its value. Has it retained its natural shape? Does it have a full canopy with many leaves and branches? If so, give it 100 percent. If not, decrease the percentage accordingly.

Add these three percentages together and divide by three. Multiply the resulting percentage by the dollar figure you noted according to the diameter above, and that will give you a good general idea of the property value of your tree.

You may want to document your tree for appraisal purposes. Record the tree's diameter, species, and age, if you know it. Take several photographs of the tree using a 50 mm ("normal") lens from a distance of 15 to 20 feet. Take several shots looking up at the tree's canopy from beside the trunk. Keep detailed records of maintenance performed on the tree for future reference.

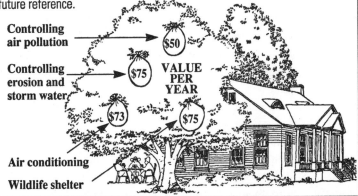

These pollutants can damage the trees, but some tree species are able to handle these chemicals better than others. The London plane tree, for example, was specifically bred to be able to deal with the smoke from coal fires in England and is able to handle and ingest elevated levels of air pollution. The white pine, on the other hand, begins to show damage—mottled needles and dying branches—right away when it is forced to metabolize toxic pollutants, especially sulfur dioxide. For that reason, the white pine is often used as an "indicator species"—a gauge for the extent of toxic pollution in the air.

The Stuttgart Experience: Trees Clean Up

Stuttgart, an industrial city in the southwestern part of Germany, used the "smog-busting" ability of trees to literally change its urban climate. It was discovered that the arrangement of buildings in the city's center served to block the wind, allowing air pollution to build up. Changes in overall city planning were instituted; some buildings were removed and tree cover was re-established. These changes significantly improved the city's air quality.

Natural Air Conditioners

People perspire; trees "evapotranspire." Water from the roots is drawn up through the cambium (the thin, moist layer just under the bark) to the leaves, where it evaporates into the air. Much like an evaporative cooler, this conversion from water to gas absorbs huge amounts of heat, cooling the hot city air. This helps explain why treeless spaces in the city are such harsh environments. It is estimated that a single large tree, such as a maple, can release up to 400 gallons of water into the atmosphere each day when water is abundant and temperature is high. Yet, when water is in short supply, trees can adapt to much lower levels.

Trees for Our Health

Just looking at a tree makes us feel better. Roger Ulrich of Texas A&M University conducted a study of patients in a suburban Pennsylvania hospital. Patients recuperating from gall bladder operations were divided into two groups: half had windows facing a brick wall; half looked onto a small stand of trees outside their windows. Those with tree views recuperated faster, stayed a shorter time in the hospital, and required fewer pain-killing injections than did the brick-wall patients.

Another study demonstrated that subjects who viewed a natural scene, even on a video monitor, reduced their physiological levels of stress much more quickly than did those who were shown a typical street scene. Most drivers, given a choice, often opt for a longer scenic drive to run errands rather than zip along the shorter, but barren, freeway route.

THE OASIS EFFECT

The shade that trees provide is much more than an aesthetic contribution or a pleasant by-product. Shade is a necessity for our cities today.

When the sun beats down on the barren concrete and black asphalt that covers so much of our urban areas, cities heat up. On

average, cities are 5 to 9 degrees Fahrenheit warmer than the rural areas that surround them, a phenomenon known as the "urban heat island." And, since these surfaces retain heat, they stay hotter longer. Once the sun goes down, these hot surfaces continue to release their stored heat until late into the evening.

Trees can make a significant dent in this build-up of heat by cooling the air and drawing less energy from overworked power plants. One study of the San Fernando Valley in Los Angeles indicated that adequate tree cover could lower temperatures there by 5 to 9 degrees. The shade that trees provide, combined with transpiration, can make individual neighborhoods—and whole cities—more pleasant. This "oasis effect," as it is called, also has very important energy-related spinoffs.

The Tucson Experience: Trees That Fit the City

Tucson, like all cities in the American West, lives with a chronic shortage of water. As its population grew, the city looked for ways to conserve its water and discovered that people were using half the municipal supply to water their lawns and gardens. The city instituted a strict set of landscape codes which encouraged people to rip out their trees and shrubs and replace them with rocks, sand, and gravel: so-called zeroscape (as opposed to Xeriscape™ gardens of drought-resistant plants).

The city began to take on a sunbaked, arid appearance. Two architects with a background in forestry, Greg McPherson and Joanne Gallaher, understood that the rocks and stones used to replace the shrubs and trees actually soaked up the sun's heat and resulted in higher surface temperatures. This, in turn, led to increased rates of evaporation from the sunbaked ground, and a jump in the amount of energy required to cool the houses. (Ironically, increased energy consumption also requires using larger amounts of water which are evaporated in the cooling towers of power plants.)

The solution, according to McPherson and Gallaher, was not to remove all vegetation but to mimic the local natural ecology and use hardy, drought-resistant plants and native trees that could withstand and thrive in Tucson's desert conditions. A single mulberry tree, a popular but thirsty choice in the area for landscaping, required enough water to keep eight palo verde trees, a local variety, in good health. Moreover, as one study indicated, every dollar invested in caring for a tree returned $2.68 worth of benefits from reduced air-conditioning energy savings, dust reduction, and the slowing of storm-water runoff. Today, Tucson is changing its appearance as its citizens become aware of the ecologically oriented opportunities of their urban forest.

The Oasis Effect at Home

Three well-placed trees around your home can provide shade that will lower cooling costs by 10 to 50 percent. Planting deciduous trees on the southeast, south, and west sides of your house will protect it from the summer sun. Besides the obvious savings in money, this conservation of energy translates directly

to less carbon dioxide produced at the generating plant that provides the energy to cool your house. Trees can also serve as windbreaks, resulting in lower heating costs during the winter. A double row of evergreen trees on the northwest side (or the side with prevailing winter winds) will protect the house in the winter. These trees can be placed away from the house at a distance of two to four times the expected height of the trees and still be effective windbreaks.

Oasis Savings Across the City and the Nation

The properly planned introduction of trees throughout a city to create an adequate canopy can realize savings of 4 percent for heating and 10 percent for cooling. Multiply those figures by the number of cities around the country, and energy savings nationwide can reach more than $2 billion a year. In fact, trees are already earning their keep. Money saved on energy in the United States during 1989, thanks to well-placed trees, exceeded the gross timber receipts from national forest timber sales.

SLOWING THE WIND AND RAIN

The presence of trees in a city can cut down on the speed of breezes and diminish wind-tunnel effects. Landscape architect Anne Whiston Spirn relates the case of a high-rise apartment complex for the elderly in Dayton, Ohio: the area was so windy that residents were afraid to leave their buildings on days when ice patches covered the sidewalks outside the buildings' entrances. Awnings and different configurations of trees and walls were set up on the walkways, but with no success: the wind continued to gust dangerously, preventing ice from melting.

When Spirn stepped back and looked at the city as a whole, it became clear that large, open parking lots on the northwest edge of Dayton allowed the winds to hit the apartment complex full force. Once trees were planted on the offending parking lots, the wind softened enough for the new controls on the apartment site to work.

Decreased wind has benefits in seasons other than winter: less windy cities mean less dust in the air—a blessing for people who are sensitive to dust or allergic to pollen. Studies in China, for example, have shown that the incidence of eye cataracts decreases when the amount of dust in the air drops. For that reason, the government there has promoted a widespread tree-planting program to cut down on the winds that blow through many of the nation's cities. During the spring of 1982, the Chinese planted a belt of trees several thousand miles long, equal to the length of the Great Wall. Citizens there were required by law to plant at least three trees a year unless they were ill or infirm. This communal tree-planting was designed to counteract the dust storms that blew from the Gobi Desert, covering everything in Beijing indoors and out.

Who Will Stop the Rain?

In a rural forest, rain is slowed and filtered by the forest canopy. In an urban forest, trees serve much the same purpose. In areas barren of trees, rainfall builds up more quickly, requiring more expensive drainage systems, and runoff can overpower storm drains, leading to local flooding and soil erosion. In neighborhoods where trees are well established, the raindrops are slowed down as they wend their way through the natural labyrinth of leaves, twigs, and branches. As a result, the storm water reaches the ground more slowly and has a greater chance to soak into the soil, replenishing both surface moisture levels and underground water tables.

The Chesapeake Experience

One study of the Gunpowder Falls Basin, part of the Chesapeake Bay watershed, illustrates the importance of trees in controlling storm water. The natural forestland produced about 50 tons of sediment for each square mile in any given year. Urban and suburban land produced 50 to 100 tons; farmland, 1,000 to 5,000 tons; and land stripped for construction, 25,000 to 50,000 tons (a thousandfold increase over the natural forest.) This sediment enters the ocean, clouds the water, and cuts off oxygen from algae and fish. Trees, especially along the water's edge, could prevent this destructive runoff of sediment.

Pacific Runoff

In the Los Angeles basin, storm-water runoff from the city's streets is one of the major sources of ocean pollution. During the eight-month-long summer dry season, dust, oil, and grease build up on the city's many streets, freeways, and parking lots. When the heavy winter rains come, often several inches in a matter of days, this toxic accumulation is washed down the catch basins directly into the Pacific Ocean. It is estimated that a program of extensive tree planting, combined with a series of other measures, could significantly cut this flow. One study of a watershed in San Francisco, for example, indicated that parking lots and commercial buildings constituted only 11 percent of the total land area. Yet planting trees in local parking lots and guiding the rainfall to the trees' roots and small porous greenbelt areas on the parking lots would lower the area's total grease and oil from storm runoff by more than 50 percent.

FIGHTING A NUMBERS GAME

Despite the unarguable global and local benefits of trees in cities, our urban forests are at grave risk. One nationwide study of street trees indicated that little more than one tree out of seven is considered to be "large," and seven out of ten have been in the ground only a few years.

In another arresting study carried out from 1975 through 1985, one-half of the cities surveyed reported that they were losing four trees to disease or age for every new tree planted. Many other cities reported a lower ratio; they were planting a single tree for every eight that died or were removed. In short, almost every city in the country recorded a drop in the number of trees along their streets. New York City, for example, watched its street-tree population drop from one million to 700,000 in a period of only ten years.

City-owned trees, such as the street species studied, only comprise some 10 to 15 percent of a city's urban forest, but they are the clearest indicators of its health. The trend across the nation is clear: we are losing our urban forests. Diseases have ravaged the tall and gracious trees that our grandparents planted, and we are not replacing them in adequate numbers.

Even our rural forests are facing severe problems. A welter of diseases is affecting trees everywhere, from eucalyptus in California to sugar maples in Maine. And increasingly harsh conditions in our cities—from pollution and the urban heat island syndrome—are lowering the life expectancy of our urban trees. In downtown areas, the average tree now lives no more than thirteen years.

Trees and Canaries: Warning Signs

Trees are like the canaries used to warn miners of problems of gas in the mineshafts. Canaries die quickly; trees take much longer to show signs of distress. Even so, the declining state of our urban forest makes it clear that something is seriously awry in our cities' environments, and this situation has been with us for at least the last decade.

President Bush recognized the gravity of the problem when he mentioned the plight of urban forests in his 1990 State of the Union Address with his proposed "America the Beautiful" program, aimed at doubling the number of trees in our cities. More important, Congress acted after the severity of the condition

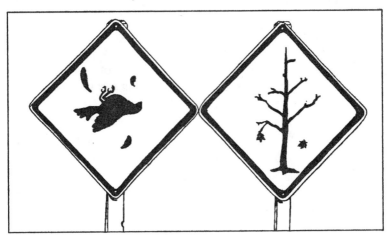

Warning: Urban forest at risk.

of our urban forests was made known, establishing new guidelines for urban forestry in the 1990 Farm Bill.

In the urban forest, every single tree is important. Much of this forest is planted by hand, one tree at a time, so it is literally true that the future of our urban forest is in our hands. Not only must we increase the number of trees, but we also have to make sure that we plant and care for them so they can grow and flourish. In a sense, we are in a race against time to increase the canopy cover, replacing hard, city concrete with the softer cover of leaves. Extending the life expectancy of our city's trees will make the impact of the urban forest on our environment even more effective.

Urban Forest Products

Once we thought of wood as the only worthwhile forest product. But as we head into the new millennium with a population of 6 billion people sharing the planet's resources, we must consider a tree's other contributions to our natural cycles— such as the reduction of carbon dioxide—as forest "products," too. In the city, these urban ecological products—including cleansing the air and providing moisture—are even more important than timber production. When you combine the environmental benefits that trees provide with their power to reduce the effects of stress on city dwellers, our urban forests are no longer an aesthetic luxury. Trees in the city are a necessity for urban health and a major factor in our global survival.

Of course, planting trees will not make all our environmental problems disappear overnight. But improving our urban forests is by no means a token action; it is an important first step and a move toward a new way of thinking about the world in which we live.

For many city dwellers, supporting urban forests or planting a single tree is also one of the few ways to approach a range of problems that are almost too overwhelming to imagine. Creating healthy urban forests is a first step toward a commitment to a healthier environment by lowering pollution levels and conserving energy. We now know that trees can change a city's environmental chemistry; they can also change the way we think about the cities we live in and improve the quality of our lives.

GETTING TO KNOW THE URBAN FOREST

Urban forests have been divided by experts into four major zones:

■ **Suburban fringes.** These are areas in which new developments exist at the edge of previously wild, open space, or former farmland. Often trees are removed to make way for streets and houses; occasionally a thoughtful developer will place houses among existing trees. In some cases, enterprising architects have actually built houses around trees, offsetting walls or rooms to accommodate them.

■ **Suburbs.** Areas in which much of the natural forest has been removed, although patches of it—around creeks, ravines, and wetlands—may survive. Trees are also found scattered among parks, private lots, and along streets. Trees in these areas may live for a century or more.

■ **City residential.** With less space for trees, the urban forest begins to thin out in this zone. Carefully tended trees grow on smaller house lots; townhouses and condominiums may have a few trees on their landscaped open areas. Parks are the only areas where stands of trees can be found, but soil is still found everywhere. Trees here live, on average, about thirty to thirty-five years. Yard trees always tend to live much longer.

■ **City center.** Consider the differences in environment between a city center and a cool forest. In one, the air is moist, the breezes gentle, the soil soft. In the other, dry winds may gust, and the sun glares down on hard, tightly packed soil. In the city center, the most hostile zone of the urban forest, trees are usually found in pots, pits, or holes. All trees must be "engineered" and tended on a regular basis. Even so, their lives are generally short and hard. Water evaporates from the ground of the city four times as fast as it does from the natural forest floor. It is no wonder that in these desertlike conditions, trees barely survive past the thirteenth year. Many foresters call this zone the center of the "urban forest doughnut."

Urban Forest vs. Rural Forest

In the past, city forests were not considered worthy of study because they were not considered "natural." Today, scientists are beginning to look at cities differently, taking all of the ecological relationships into account, including the relationship between urban forests and human activity.

The major difference between urban and wilderness forests is that wilderness forests tend to extend over larger areas of land and can therefore support a much richer and healthier diversity of plant and animal life. Where forests remain unfragmented, the trees within them can also protect one another from overexposure to sun and wind. And where the soil remains untrampled and undisturbed by grazing or logging, the wilderness forest holds the soil in place, preventing massive erosion. Although subject to natural disasters, such as fire and storms, trees tend to live much longer in rural forests than in cities. Individual trees in an undisturbed old-growth forest often continue standing long after they die, providing homes for insects, birds, and a variety of other animals. Even fallen trees continue to benefit the forest by fertilizing the forest floor and streams, as well as providing homes for many species.

Though lacking the ecological richness of the wilderness environment, urban woodlands provide many of the same kinds of benefits to the city that they do to the rural areas around them— cleaning the air, filtering water, and holding the soil in place. According to recent research from the New York Botanical Gardens in the Bronx, some trees in city parks may fare even better than their suburban cousins by using the nitrogen fallout from air pollution as a soil nutrient. In the long run, however, experts anticipate that this overfertilization by pollutants could also cause the trees to be less adaptable to drought, eventually causing them to die out. What is remarkable about this evidence, however, is how adaptable some trees can be to the worst of conditions, at least in the short run.

Animals of the Urban Forest

A forest wilderness is inhabited by a wealth of wildlife—a

community of birds, insects, reptiles, and mammals that live in and among the trees, often depending on them for their very survival. Although the urban forest contains less biological diversity than its distant woodland cousins, the animals that occupy the urban forest are still numerous, and they still need trees. We are the main inhabitants of the city forest—human beings, living in forests of our own design. And to maintain the livability of our urban forest home, we need to become its caretaker.

As we take better care of our city trees, we may also observe a change in the denizens of this healthier urban forest. For example, leafy shade trees will attract songbirds in greater numbers. In a very real sense, our choice to support the urban forest will determine whether we want to see squirrels or rats in our cities.

A Tale of Two Soils

One essential difference between the rural and urban forests is soil. Soil in the old-growth forest is ideal for the growth of trees. Loose, moist, and slightly spongy in texture, it provides water and nutrients to much of the forest's animal and plant life, including the trees themselves. This soil is protected and augmented by the layer of natural humus composed of fallen leaves and other decaying organic matter that holds moisture in the soil and minimizes erosion. In time, this natural compost will become part of the rich earth itself.

Soil in the urban forest, especially in the city center, is hardly recognizable as such. "City soil," as it is called, is often purposely compacted to increase its stability. The constant passage of traffic, even the footfalls of pedestrians, further compact the soil, making it extremely difficult for roots to grow and "breathe." City soil often has only 5 percent air space, as opposed to the 50 percent found in a natural setting, so moisture tends to run off its surface rather than soak in. As a result, city soil more closely resembles baked clay than a nourishing medium for tree roots.

City soil may also have a high lime content from nearby concrete or leaching; it often has a high salt content from winter de-icing programs; it is bombarded with used automobile oil and is often permeated with fertilizers, pesticides, and dog urine. These and many other chemical insults make city soil a very difficult growing medium for trees. And with no protective mulch layer to keep the moisture in, the soil remains hard and dry throughout much of the growing season.

Natives and Visitors

Contrary to popular belief, the trees that grow best in cities are not always the trees native to the region. The environment of the city is much different than that of the surrounding countryside. Large cities have elevated temperatures, increased wind velocities, air pollution, and compacted soils. This explains why swamp trees such as tupelo, cypress, and sycamore often do very well in city settings, since their roots are able to function in an almost airless medium.

In general, native trees are crucial indicators of the health of the urban environment: the more of them that can survive city life, the healthier the environment. However, native trees may not be the best choice for new plantings in an urban center that has been substantially denuded of its original growth. What is most important is finding the right tree for a given site. Planting hardy trees that come from other areas of the country or other continents is necessary at first. These more rugged species—including specially engineered hybrids—planted with the environment in mind can change the harsh micro-climates of cities and increase the oasis effect. Once a healthy urban forest is well established, native trees can often be reintroduced to thrive on the ground where they once flourished. Experts have estimated, however, that a shift to native trees will require a doubling of the average city's present tree canopy from one-third to two-thirds of the total urban surface.

OF TREES, SETTLERS, AND CITIES

Native Americans were the first to extend species of trees beyond their original growth areas. Tribes from the Mississippi, Ohio, and Missouri areas planted pecans hundreds of miles north of the trees' original range.

European settlers often brought with them trees that reminded them of home. Norway spruce, Scotch pine, European linden, and hornbean started showing up in cemeteries as arboreal companions for the final resting place. After more than two centuries of importing trees, the trend toward an assortment of species was already well established. Today, Washington's Mt. Vernon estate and Jefferson's Monticello feature a mixture of native, English, and hybrid tree varieties.

As the Spanish moved into California, Franciscan fathers planted olive groves. Farmers who needed fast-growing windbreaks throughout the West planted eucalyptus trees imported from Australia. Pepper trees from Brazil did well in Southern California, as did large numbers of one fruit-tree variety that would soon become identified with California: the navel orange.

As American settlers spread out over the continent, trees followed their movements. Blue spruce and Douglas fir were brought back east. In some cases, the "foreign species" did so well that they grew like opportunistic weeds, crowding out the local native trees and displacing the associated animal life that the native species supported. Elsewhere, the new species quickly adapted to their new environment without disrupting the natives.

Trees and Towns

Trees and natural vegetation were an integral part of early city planning. Towns in the thirteen colonies introduced trees to the "common green" for all to enjoy. In 1807, the territory of Michigan specified that trees were to be planted on the streets of Detroit. A few decades later, lots in middle-class areas were large enough to support growth of the larger native species, especially chestnut, elm, and maple. By the turn of the century, almost every city street in the country was graced with the shade and stately forms of these spreading giants. In addition, many exotic trees were introduced from abroad, both intentionally and by accident.

In 1910, an airborne fungus descended upon the chestnut population, wiping out that species from much of its habitat. Then it was the elm's turn. Crown wilt among city elms was observed in 1930, the first sign of Dutch elm disease. Spread by a tiny beetle, the plague ravaged the continent, and half a century later only a small fraction of America's elms had escaped the plague.

As populations and mass housing burgeoned from the 1930s on, smaller city lots could not accommodate large trees. The trees were removed and, in most cases, never replaced. This treeless trend, combined with the sad demise of the elm and other species in our cities, resulted in a drastic drop in the number of trees in the urban forest from the 1950s on. The trees our grandparents planted had disappeared, and we had done little to replace them.

With ever-increasing populations and more air pollution, the tree canopies of our cities diminished, and average city temperatures rose 5 to 10 degrees Fahrenheit. By the late 1970s, the need for trees in towns and cities was clear. A group of

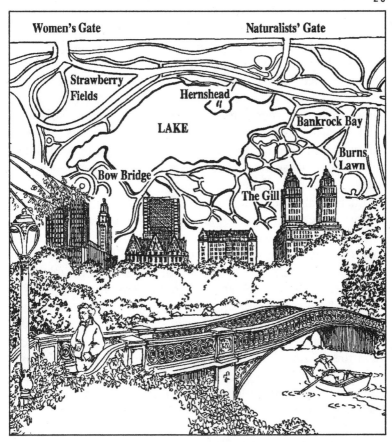

Central Park in New York City was designed as a respite for urban workers.

farsighted foresters turned their attention to the city, and the modern concept of urban forestry was born.

Parks: A Breath of Fresh Air in the City

Trees have always played an important part in the lives of cities. According to paintings found in tombs, the Egyptians used trees with the same regular geometrical approach employed in the construction of their temples. "I have planted trees and shrubs to the end that the people should sit under their shade," reads one inscription from the tomb of Ramses III. Assyrians planted trees in rows to create parks as long ago as 700 B.C.

Private Renaissance gardens were often embellished with cypress trees, while public plazas were left treeless. It was in seventeenth-century France that the public use of trees was developed into an art form. City designers in Paris drew upon the heritage of baroque gardens where trees had been planted radially outward from forests to make shooting game easier. City streets, oriented radially around central plazas and lined with trees, replicated this arrangement. Versailles, the seat of power, was adorned throughout with the regular placement of trees.

In England geometrical gardens were not the fashion. Instead, so-called country parks were planted with "natural" groupings of trees in an attempt to replicate the idyllic views of country scenes. This re-creation of the world of nature was the expression of sentimental pastoralism, a school of thought that, in America, went back at least to the Revolutionary days. Thomas Jefferson, for example, felt that cities represented evil while small rural towns were morally superior. In the late 1850s, American landscape architects Frederick L. Olmsted and Calvert Vaux drew heavily upon this tradition and that of the English country parks when they designed Central Park in New York City primarily to give working people a pastoral escape from their oppressive city dwellings.

SEEING THE FOREST AND ITS TREES

As we enter a new millennium, the division between human beings and nature continues to dominate most people's thinking. The concept of the urban forest is, in many ways, an attempt to eliminate this separation, encouraging people who live and work in the city to appreciate, support, and care for trees everywhere in their midst—near buildings and in parking lots, along streets and greenbelts, as well as in city parks and in their own backyards. Properly nurtured, the urban forest can become an integral part of our daily lives and the lives of generations to come. Urban forests represent, in a very real sense, the relationship of human beings to nature as a whole, and are the foundation for a new way of thinking about what cities can be and how we inhabit them.

PART II:

PLANTING YOUR TREE

THE RIGHT TREE IN THE RIGHT PLACE

In a sense, planting even one tree is much like having a family—it's a long-term commitment. Chances are, you will be living with the trees you choose to plant for decades to come, so before you plant, look forward to a fair degree of planning, a touch of design, sensible ground preparation and, of course, loving care once the tree is in the ground. A few preliminary steps will provide you with a lifetime of beauty and benefits.

A little planning goes a long way, as the following two tales illustrate:

The Greeners

Joan and Harry Greener watch the flock of birds that gather in their maple tree each sunset. In the ten years since they planted it, the maple has grown up perfectly on the southern side of their house, gently shading it during the hottest part of the day. Its two companions, an oak and a birch, stand proudly on the western side of the house, gently filtering the last of the sun's rays.

The couple planted their trees for both beauty and utility. Joan once figured they were saving more than 20 percent on their summer electricity bill now that the trees had grown tall enough to shade their house. The double row of pines on the northern edge of their property also made a big difference during the winter. No longer did their windows rattle when the arctic winds swept down from Canada, and Harry no longer had to shovel through 4-foot-high snow drifts. Last year, after Harry put in some inexpensive weather stripping and added insulation to their attic, Joan estimated a 10 percent savings on their winter heating costs, too. Yet far more than the money they saved, the Greeners appreciated the double row of pines for the sense of privacy it gave them. That line of pines seemed to muffle the sound of cars from the street and shielded their property with a gentle wall of greenery that still allowed the blue of the sky to filter through.

The Greeners had spent a lot of time planning the trees now growing in their yard. They recalled the trips with their children to the tree nurseries and the arboretum, and the discussions they had before planting. Now Harry made sure he pruned regularly. He also called out a professional one year when insects bored into the tips of the branches, causing the outer edges of the trees to die. All that effort was paying off. With the bird song in the air and a lively, verdant palette in their yard, the whole family felt as if their house had been built in the center of a forest grove that had been there forever.

The Uproots

Bert and Barbara Uproot shake their heads as they examine the sycamore they planted seven years ago. The nursery owner had recommended it highly as a fast grower, which it was—but he may have oversold the virtues of the tree. Already its roots had cracked their driveway and lifted one section a good inch above the others.

The couple had moved to this neighborhood the same year as the Greeners across the street, but their property had none of the lush look of their neighbors' yard. At the edge of their lot line stood a row of Lombardy poplars. Last week the utility company came and had to lop off the top 10 feet to prevent them from growing into the power lines overhead. They should not have been planted there. Now they looked stunted and ugly.

Barbara had always had a fondness for willows, but no more. The delicate sapling they planted in their front yard, directly in front of the picture window, was now a full-blown disaster that blocked their view of the street completely and left the living room in perpetual shadow. And the two pear trees in the back-yard, bought at an end-of-season sale at a nursery, had never really grown in properly. They looked ragged and produced little or no fruit. The Uproots liked trees as much as anyone. What were they doing wrong?

STEP ONE: EXPLORING THE URBAN FOREST

You know you want to plant trees, but which ones? The answer to this most difficult question can be addressed in terms of the specific benefits you want them to provide. In a sense, every tree on your lot meets a need or fulfills a set of demands. Consider your trees as necessary to your home as your driveway, garage, or roof. So, to derive the best possible benefits from your trees, it is wise to decide beforehand exactly what purpose you wish them to fulfill. What do you want your trees to do for you?

Finding the Trees for Your Forest
(even if you only have one planting space)

Some trees are best suited for producing shade. If shade is what you're looking for, what kind of tree is best? Deciduous trees (trees that lose their leaves in winter) such as maples and oaks, with their spreading branches and dense canopies, will provide solid shade. Others, such as honey locust and willows, will create feathery shadows. Perhaps you want to screen an unsightly view. Staggered rows of conifers (evergreen trees) will grow in quickly, define your space, and provide a more natural

---

When Does a Tree Die?

The lives of plants are quite different from those of animals in a number of basic ways, including growth patterns. Trees cannot heal their own wounds, so when a healthy, living tree is damaged, the injured parts fall off and the tree grows new parts. Trees renew themselves continually, not only as the seasons change, but throughout their life spans. This is why correctly pruning a tree stimulates new growth. When more parts of the plant are dying than growing, the productive life of the tree is over. When rapid-growing trees shed larger branches, they become dangerous and lose their value as good neighbors.

---

border; a single row, on the other hand, will only outline a border and give a sense of privacy. Learning a little about landscaping techniques will provide a lot of options.

Looking Around: Tree-watching 101

Trees certainly enhance any property, but how they do that depends on their size, shape, and location on the lot. While it is possible to hire an expert who can design a plan for your yard, this is usually an expensive option. Instead, you can design your own tree landscaping and, in the process, get to know the trees and the urban forest that surround you.

One good first step is to take a walk or bicycle ride to see what your neighbors have done with trees. Think of your city as a living catalog of trees, an arboretum right at your doorstep. Begin to notice the different shapes and sizes of trees in your area (see page 39). Spend a little time getting a feel for the way trees can help give a sense of scale to a house or a sense of unity to a yard or lot. Look especially for trees in lots with houses that are similar to your own. What have other homeowners chosen to do with their landscaping? What works and what doesn't? Which arrangement of trees looks graceful and inviting? Which appears crowded and close?

Types of Planting Stock

	How Sold	How to Plant
Bare root (BR) 	With roots in moisture-holding medium such as peat or moss.	Spread roots over soil mound at bottom of planting hole and cover with soil immediately.
Balled & burlapped (B&B)	With roots contained in ball of soil that's wrapped with burlap, cloth, chicken wire, etc.	Lift tree by soil ball and center in planting area. Stabilize with backfill, then remove burlap around sides of soil ball. Add backfill and water to settle soil.
Containered stock 	With roots in container that can range from 1/2 to 10, 20, or more gallons.	Same as for B&B, or remove container before placing soil mass in planting hole. Eliminate circling roots by laying rootball on its side, slicing with a knife.
Tree-spade transplants 	With roots in native soil. Cost includes moving and planting.	A tree spade digs and moves the tree in one operation. Otherwise, treat like B&B minus the burlap when planting.

Advantages	Disadvantages
• Least expensive. • Easiest to handle. • Roots adapt to existing soil better than B&B planting. • Not practical for large plants.	• Roots prone to desiccation if not kept moist during transplanting.
• Less expensive than container or tree-spade transplants. • Better survival rate than BR stock, for amateur planter.	• Harder to handle than BR stock due to weight of soil ball.
• Slightly easier to handle than B&B. • Better survival rate than BR because it is generally a year older.	• Same as for B&B. • Circling roots very common. • Root problems likely if tree is too large for the pot.
• Useful for moving large trees or when nursery is close to planting site. • Instant landscape.	• May be expensive. • If size of tree is not matched to tree-spade size, or if tree is taken from the woods, tree may lose too many roots.

In addition, notice the different species of trees that seem to thrive in your area. This is your clearest indication of what will grow best around your home. You may want to carry a tree-identification guide with you, available from the U.S. Department of Agriculture or your local bookstore. Or take note of any imported varieties you particularly like and make a simple sketch of the shape of the tree and its leaves so you can identify it later. If there is an arboretum in your area, pay a visit—it will be fun and educational. You might also knock on your neighbors' doors and ask them what kind of trees they have. Chances are, they will be able to tell you something about the history and any problems they may have had with their trees. They may also be able to recommend nurseries or tree-care companies. You may find that most homeowners are as proud—or disappointed—with their choice of trees as they are with their choice of pets.

Fast Growers, Slow Growers

Trees grow at different rates. Some species, such as eucalyptus, silver maple, cottonwood, and poplar are easily established and, in full sunlight, can grow several feet a year—these are the fast growers. A sycamore planted in an ideal spot can grow to over 100 feet tall and 3 feet in diameter in forty years. Others, such as oaks, hard maples, beech, spruce, fir, and hemlock, grow more slowly, but provide more long-term benefits.

Fast-growing trees have their disadvantages. They have "weaker wood" than their slow-growing cousins, an attribute that may leave your yard littered with branches and twigs in windy weather. And they may have aggressive root systems that get in the way. Fast-growing varieties also have much shorter life spans. A hybrid poplar, for example, can establish itself on a difficult site and still grow rapidly, but will only make a good yard tree for twenty to thirty years and will require more maintenance along the way. An oak or a fir, on the other hand, can still be around for your grandchildren's children.

Plant slow-growing varieties closer to buildings or high-use areas, such as a picnic table or children's play area. You can also

The Shape of Trees

From a design point of view, planting trees around your home is an art form with the shapes and colors of nature as your palette. Look at the shapes of the trees in your neighborhood and surrounding areas. The spacing and arrangement of the different tree shapes can enhance the appearance of a house and give it a sense of scale and personality. To help understand how a tree will change the look of your property, consider its placement in your yard in relation to its shape when fully grown, not how it looks as a sapling in the nursery.

There are trees at your local nurseries well suited for any available space on your property. Thanks to the science of tree breeding, you can find deciduous trees in many shapes. Narrow spaces between buildings are well suited for tall, columnar trees, such as columnar red or Norway maple, or even an English oak. A broad, open area would be better suited for the proverbial spreading chestnut tree.

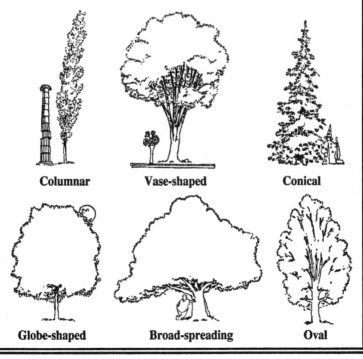

Columnar	Vase-shaped	Conical
Globe-shaped	Broad-spreading	Oval

mix the slow- and fast-growing trees, making sure that there is adequate sunlight for the slower varieties. This will provide you with quick cover for the first few years, while allowing the slower trees to get established. When the oaks and firs have settled in, you can remove the fast-growing trees to allow the slow growers to reach their full size.

Knowing the purposes of your trees will help narrow down your choices. It is also important that the trees you choose are suitable to your local climatic and soil conditions.

Checking Out Your Soil

Soils differ according to how wet or dry they are. In addition, they vary widely according to their degree of acidity or alkalinity. Much of the country has problems with overly acidic soil. Alkaline soils are more often found in arid and semiarid areas where the low rainfall doesn't allow the natural salts in the soil to leach, or soak through, properly. Some trees do much better in one kind of soil than another: most pines, for example, prefer loose, dry, acidic soil—they don't like wet feet. Trees such as the palo verde, bur oak, or desert willow can thrive, once they are established in the dry alkaline soils of the Southwest.

If you are not familiar with the condition of the soil in your region, obtain a soil survey from the Soil Conservation Service. Every county in the nation has a district office, and their information is free. (Look under U.S. Government in your local phone book for the county office.) The surveys tell basic information about the soils. Unfortunately, the more urban your location, the more your soil is likely to be changed by construction activities. You should do some checking on your own. Some aspects of your soil that are worth investigating before you plant a tree are: acidity, density, moisture content, and structure. Kits to test the acidity or alkalinity of soil are usually available at retail nurseries or garden centers.

Wet or dry? The amount of water in your soil will often determine which trees will grow best there. You can purchase meters at garden centers to test the moisture content of your soil, although it is also possible to determine this with a simple test.

Dig a hole about 1 foot deep, and fill it with water. If it takes more than an hour to drain, you have a drainage problem and will have wet soil anytime it rains. The structure of the soil plays a role in drainage and plant growth. If you grab a handful of soil and can't form it into a ball, it is probably too dry—and possibly too sandy. If the earth sticks to your shovel when digging, does not crumble easily, and leaves water on your palm when squeezed into a ball, it is definitely on the wet, clay side. Soils with an abundance of clay have drainage problems. In addition, overly wet soils often have a "sour" or slightly "rotten" odor. Healthy soil smells more like the rich leaf cover found on the floor of a healthy forest.

City soils. City soils—wet or dry, acid or alkaline—are particularly unsuited for tree planting. In many cases they have been compressed, either on purpose or by the constant passage of bulldozers. In some cases, they may also have been sterilized. (This is common practice on school playgrounds.) If the ground you are considering for planting has the consistency of a lead brick and is more suited to a pick or jackhammer than a shovel, you may have to spend a lot of time returning the soil in your yard to a condition that will ensure tall, healthy trees.

Take a shovel to your yard and dig a few test pits. If the soil is compact and does not dig easily, rent a rototiller and begin working to improve the planting area. Your rewards will be well worth the effort. One robust tree thriving in well-prepared soil is more beneficial to you and to the urban forest at large than three trees struggling to live in harsh urban conditions.

Planting Trees with Impact: Energy Conservation

It is always easy to identify the site of a farmhouse on the landscape from miles away—just look for the trees. The early pioneers understood the benefits of trees and planted them strategically around their homes as windbreaks and blessed protection from a blazing summer sun. We can follow their lead in our post-modern cities, even improving on their methods with a few high-tech adjustments.

A tree's ability to shade your house in summer and shield you from cold winds in winter will put money in your pockets.

42

Planting for energy savings

Leafy trees properly planted on the south and west sides of a house can shade it from the summer sun, while welcoming cooling breezes. In winter, a windbreak of conifers on the northwest side will buffer the coldest winds, while the bare branches of the deciduous trees will allow the warming sun to get through. (Circles indicate the "path of the sun" in summer and winter, respectively.)

Researchers in California, Pennsylvania, and Florida have measured the energy-saving value of trees around a house to be 10 to 50 percent of the air-conditioning bill. Even the Internal Revenue Service recognizes that a shade tree can be appraised in terms of the cost of constructing a structure that would provide equivalent shade. In 1975, that amount worked out to more than three dollars per square foot of shade. Today, it would be even more.

Most of us will not claim our shade trees on our tax returns. More important than the hard cash savings and increased real-estate appraisal value of trees is the fact that trees lessen our demand for energy to both cool and heat our homes. And when we demand less energy, power plants need to burn less fossil fuel to generate that energy, and so we can reduce the amount of carbon dioxide spewed into our atmosphere. Each household's contribution to this global commitment is crucial. Well-planned trees planted for energy conservation nationwide would create a reduction of carbon dioxide in the atmosphere by several million tons per year through energy conservation, in addition to the tree's ability to absorb nitrogen and carbon dioxide directly. And those millions of tons are built up one pound at a time, one tree at a time, one house at a time. The trees you plant will help.

To Lend a Little Shade

Plant varieties of trees that will grow tall and dense enough to shade the southeast and southwest areas of your roof and walls for as long as possible during the height of summer. You may have to wait several years before the trees reach optimum height.

If you live in the north, use deciduous trees that shed their leaves in the fall. These trees will provide shade in the summer, but allow the sun to filter through the branches and warm the house in the winter. In the south, trees can be green year-round, and the need for year-round shade is especially important there. Trees or shrubs should also shade your external air-conditioning unit, if you have one.

Even in moderate climates, the temperature of your house will remain more comfortable throughout the year if you plant at least three trees on the south, southeast, and southwest exposures.

Combine your trees with a variety of vines and shrubs, especially on south-facing walls, which help shade and control the heat. One idea is to plant shrubs which respond well to pruning in front of south-facing windows. You can trim them back in winter, allowing the sun to warm the house, then let them grow taller in summer for cooling shade. As your landscaping skill improves, you can find many other ways to fine-tune your energy savings—including directing summer and winter breezes—with trees and shrubs.

Windbreaks in Winter

As a general rule, trees are effective windbreaks for a distance about four times their height. The average lot would require trees about 50 feet from the side of the house on the same side as the direction of the prevailing winds. In most areas of the country, prevailing winds come from the northwest. If you are in doubt about prevailing winds, phone the National Weather Service, General Information, at (301) 713-0622, or contact your local radio station or television weather channel.

In the north, plant your trees in the path of the most vicious winter winds, using staggered rows of evergreens to create a more effective wind barrier. In the south, windbreaks are equally effective for quelling hot breezes. While we tend to associate summer zephyrs with cooling, the movement of hot or very warm air over exterior walls actually heats buildings. One study showed that shrubs and trees used in combination to both shade and block the wind could result in savings as high as 75 percent in warmer areas of the country. The key was the use of shrubs. Allow them to grow high and block the wind during the hottest part of the year; when temperatures drop, trim them back to allow the cooler air to strike the house and moderate interior temperatures.

STEP TWO: PLANNING YOUR LANDSCAPE

Once you have an idea of which trees are thriving in your neighborhood, and after you have done enough tree reconnaissance to develop a familiarity with trees and how they might help you conserve energy, it is time to make a plan of your house and lot. Draw it approximately to scale, and indicate all the structures, including paths and walkways, and any trees already on your property. Indicate the points of the compass on your drawing in order to determine where best to place trees for shade and windbreaks (see illustrations on pages 42 and 48).

Thinking Ahead

Don't forget to indicate the presence of power and telephone poles and wires, if any. If you are going to dig more than a foot deep where cables might be buried, check with your local utility companies. Call the utility's information service in your telephone

Mix and Match: Groves and Orchards

If you want a few large spreading trees, make sure there is adequate room for them all to grow; plan on at least 20 feet between tree trunks. In planting groups of trees of different varieties set closer together, be aware that available light is a powerful determinant of the ultimate shape of each individual tree and will affect the look of the grove when mature. A small opening, or "window" of light, between trees will encourage the trees to grow taller rather than expending their energy in creating a broad canopy, as they would in the open. Once the tree has achieved the desired height, you can thin the group of trees, as you would carrots in a garden, to modify the shape of a tree. The crowns of the trees will expand to capture the energy provided by the bigger window of light after the thinning.

book or the customer service number on your utility bill. It's also a good idea to try to keep a tree's roots away from your sewer lines. Roots can get into leaky pipes and clog them up. This is especially common in areas where clay pipe is still being used. Investigating this potential problem in advance may save you unwanted and costly maintenance in years to come.

Planning for Wildlife

Trees attract wildlife. Birds nest in the branches, and animals find shelter within the trees of the urban forest. This fauna bring with them a badly needed sense of the untamed world into the confines of the city. Watching a squirrel collect nuts and seeds while gold and scarlet leaves flutter to the ground is a living example of the change of seasons. Rabbit tracks near a pine tree dusted white after a fresh snowfall is a picture-book vision of winter. And the welcome sound of robins chirping in trees adorned with pale-green leaf buds or cherry blossoms will always be a cheerful reminder that spring has sprung.

So, while planning your treescape, think of the animals. The two key elements in bringing wildlife to your property are food

A Sense of Design

When considering the design of the landscape around your home, why not borrow a few basic principles from the professionals? Here are a few to get you started:

❑ **Mass plantings:** Once you locate a good spot for a tree, create a planting bed and use a group of trees along with shrubs in the same area.

❑ **Border plantings:** Use planting areas to create a border or frame for outdoor-living areas, walkways, or special views. (This way of considering spatial arrangement is different —and more visually interesting—than simply using trees along the edge of your property line.) Plants can visually enlarge your patio area or brighten the path leading to your front door.

❑ **Complementary plantings:** Planting beds can be used to soften the sharp edges of a house and bring a tall corner of a building down to ground level. A few trees near the house with shrubs of various sizes at their bases create a handsome complementary arrangement.

❑ **Windbreaks and backdrops:** Use evergreens for windbreaks or as a backdrop for flowering plants. Their dark green branches will show off the flowers.

and shelter. Trees supply both. Consider the possibility of having some fruit or nut trees in your yard. They provide excellent food for the animals who live in the urban forest, including your family, and, most likely, your neighbors, too. The more variety, including size and shape—as well as species—of plants, the more the animals will like it. Even if you have bird feeders, your feathered friends prefer branches close to the food for protection.

Flowering trees, especially, are also a treat for the eyes. In Japan, the arrival of the cherry blossoms is a time for celebration. Whole families trek to the parks to picnic among the flowering

Ten Questions to Ask Yourself Before Choosing a Tree

① What is the purpose of this tree? Shade, windbreak, landscaping, ground retention?

② Will it conflict with any overhead wires, underground cables, or sewers?

③ What will this tree look like when fully grown?

④ How long will it take the tree to reach its full size?

⑤ What are the physical characteristics of the tree: tall or short, falling leaves or flowers, fall color?

⑥ Does this tree grow well where I live?

⑦ Is it far enough away from the house, the sidewalk, the neighbors, and other trees?

⑧ Will it block any windows when it reaches its full size?

⑨ How will it fit in with the plants, structures, and other trees already on my property? (Will it drop leaves in a swimming pool or shade a vegetable garden?)

⑩ What kind of special care, if any, does it require?

trees, and poets write traditional spring verses about them. You may not be so literary about your trees, although you might well be inspired to write a few lines at blossom time. A flowering fruit tree in your yard can provide the practical gifts of shade and food. It can also be a visual reminder of the rhythms of the seasons, from the blossoms in spring, to summer fruits, to the jam-making at harvest time, to the elegant bare branches in winter. With the wide variety of dwarf and semi-dwarf varieties now available, you can probably enjoy the many benefits of a fruit tree no matter where you live.

Sketching It In

Select the sites for your chosen trees and draw circles to represent their canopies—and root systems—when fully grown. This will make it easier to determine how far apart you can plant your new trees. It might help to lay a piece of tracing paper over your lot plan and experiment with different arrangements of trees.

One good way to visualize how trees will look on your property is to take a few photographs of your house, one from each side, if possible. Then overlay tracing paper and draw shapes of trees and shrubs in the areas where you are considering them—or cut out the shapes from construction paper and move them around to picture the full effect.

If you are especially creative, you may want to make a rough three-dimensional model of your house from cardboard, and use cutout models of trees to determine where you want them to be. Plasticene clay will hold the model and trees upright and in place. This tree-planning stage is an activity the whole family can enjoy. Children are delighted to be included especially if they are able to choose and later plant and care for their own tree.

STEP THREE: SHOPPING FOR YOUR TREE

Visiting a nursery can be an enjoyable or a confusing and expensive experience, depending on how much homework you've done and how clear you are about what you are looking for. You may want to visit several different nurseries at first, depending on where you live, to become familiar with the quality and variety of each nursery's stock, as well as to compare prices, service, and the expertise of their staff. Then, when you're sure you know what you want, you can go back to the nursery of your choice to select and purchase your tree.

Questions you should be able to answer before going to the nursery:
❑ **What are some of the trees that do well in my area?**
Have a list in hand before going to the nursery, so you won't be confused by all the varieties available.
❑ **What are the planting conditions in my area—wet or dry, acidic or alkaline?**
Be prepared to confirm these facts with the nursery staff and check them off your list as trees are discussed.
❑ **How big a tree can I carry home and plant?**
You have two things to consider: tree height and the weight of the root ball. Trees are sold by the caliper inch (the diameter of the trunk measured 6 inches above the ground). One person can lift a 1-inch caliper tree, and the largest tree that two people can lift is 2-1/2 inches.

Inquiries to make once you get to the nursery:
❑ Ask for a list of the trees they have in stock, showing size and price.
❑ Explain your planting needs and get recommendations, marking possible trees on the inventory list.
❑ Look at the potential trees to determine their quality.

❏ Ask if the tree you are considering is "grown to nursery standards." The American Association of Nurserymen publishes a set of standards for preparing nursery stock for sale. If the nursery doesn't know, then go elsewhere.
❏ Is the tree a clone (grown from a cutting or bud graft), or is it grown from seed? If you need a specific shape, you probably want a clone. If it is a bud graft, beware of sprouts near the base of the tree; only the grafted bud should grow from there.
❏ What is the mature height, width, and shape of the tree?
❏ What do the leaves, seeds, and flowers look like?

Once you are satisfied that you have chosen the right tree for your property, you should check to make sure you have everything you need for planting and taking care of it.

Tools of the Trade

Garden tools. Here are some of the garden tools you may need to plant and care for your tree:
❏ spade and shovel
❏ rake
❏ rototiller (especially if ground is hard)
❏ wire cutters
❏ pliers
❏ watering hose
❏ pruning shears
❏ pruning saw (necessary after the first few years of growth)

Soil amendments. Most city soils can benefit from amendments. (Remember to add amendments to a large area around a tree, not just in the planting hole.) Here are some of the best to choose from:
❏ peat moss
❏ leaf mulch, bark, or old sawdust

Mulch. Use it around all trees and shrubs.

Stakes. For young trees, you will need:
- ❏ flexible stakes
- ❏ bicycle inner tube, old nylon stockings, or old garden hose

And . . .
- ❏ Polypropylene tree shelter, if you are growing small trees (less than 2 feet high).

STEP FOUR: PREPARATION AND PLANTING

After you have selected your tree and purchased whatever supplies you need, it is time to prepare the ground to receive its new resident.

Preparing the Soil

If your soil requires extensive amendments and/or watering, you may want to complete this preparation before bringing the

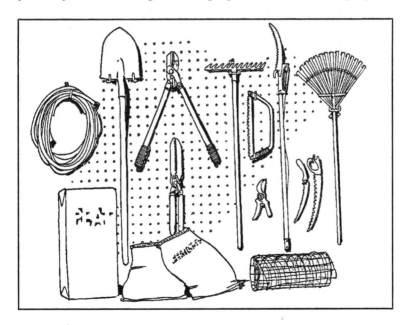

tree home from the nursery. If your soil is quite dry, water the area thoroughly first, and let it soak in for a day or so. This will also make it easier to dig.

Rich soil. If you are one of the very few city dwellers lucky enough to be planting your trees in rich, undisturbed soil, simply dig a hole just big enough for the root ball and slide the tree in. For best results, the tree should be set as low in the ground as it was at the nursery—but no lower. You can usually see the old soil line by examining the root collar or the area where the trunk widens and changes color before becoming roots and backfill. After planting, spread mulch 2 to 4 inches deep around the tree, beginning about 6 inches or so away from the trunk and stopping as far from the trunk as at least twice the diameter of the root ball. Then water liberally, allowing the water to settle the soil rather than tamping it down with your feet.

City soil. Most of us will have to contend with soil that is often highly compacted and consequently much denser and harder than undisturbed soil. The tree's roots will have difficulty growing through such soil, so simply digging a hole slightly larger than the root ball will restrict the roots to a small space and shorten the life of your tree. Recent research has shown that the modern urban forest requires a dramatically different approach to planting trees than was previously assumed: Instead of digging a hole, you need to prepare a planting area. Since most of the roots of a tree grow within the top one foot of soil, it is crucial to prepare a much wider but shallower area of soil before planting trees in the average urban-residential location—a front lawn, side yard, or backyard.

Ten Steps to the Perfectly Planted Yard Tree

1 **Mark it.** For most house lots, prepare a planting area as deep as the root ball of your chosen tree and three to five times the root ball's diameter—the wider the better (see illustration on page 53). You can mark the perimeter of this circle with the edge of your shovel.

2 **Prepare it.** We recommend using a rototiller, especially if you are not used to gardening. You can rent these machines

on a daily basis. They will save time and prevent a myriad of blisters and backaches. You can improve this loosened soil within the rooting area by adding organic matter: leaf mulch or commercially available products such as manure. If you do add amendments, however, make the planting area on the larger side and amend all of it. Improving the soil only around the tree roots will restrict root growth. Approach fertilizers with caution; they can damage the roots of newly planted trees. A balanced mix of nitrogen, phosphorous, and potassium—such as 10-10-10 (percentages for each element, respectively)—can be beneficial, but the nitrogen must be "slow release." If this is not stated on the package, don't use it. Use 3 pounds per inch of tree diameter and mix well with the loosened soil.

3 **Free it.** If you have a container-grown tree, remove the roots from the plastic bucket or container. Rapping the container smartly with your hand will help the roots come out. Be prepared to cut the container open if necessary. Check to see if the roots have grown in circles within the confines of the

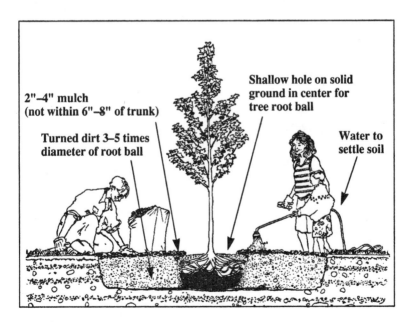

2"–4" mulch
(not within 6"–8" of trunk)

Shallow hole on solid ground in center for tree root ball

Turned dirt 3–5 times diameter of root ball

Water to settle soil

container. If so, try to disentangle and spread them out. If they are too thick or well established to unravel by hand, cut and free them. Encircling, or "girdling," roots, as they are known, will strangle the tree in later years if left unattended. The roots found at the top of the container need the most attention.

4 **Dig it.** Dig a shallow hole in the center of the prepared circle, and set the root ball on solid ground within this hole—not on loose soil. This is important to fully support the weight of the young tree and prevent it from sinking into the ground. The new ground surface should be level with the original soil line. (Check the tree's base for the original soil line.) Place a board across the hole to line it up.

One exception to this method is if the ground has poor drainage—heavy clay soil, for instance. In that case, make sure the root ball is 1 or 2 inches *above* the surrounding soil; then raise the soil level of the tree's new home to match this new level. The final soil line should meet the tree at the same location it did at the nursery.

5 **Release it.** Cut any wires or rope securing the burlap around the root ball, especially at the base of the trunk. Spread the burlap out and place the wires at a distance from the roots to be buried. Don't leave any burlap exposed above ground; it will act as a wick, drawing moisture up and away from the tree's roots. If you fertilize, use only slow-release fertilizer in the planting hole.

6 **Fill it.** Backfill the hole with the soil that you originally dug out. The level of the soil should come up to the root collar (top of the root ball), but no higher. Don't tamp it down.

7 **Unwrap it.** Remove any trunk wrapping, unless the tree's bark has been damaged. The thread used to hold this wrapping in place can kill the tree as the trunk grows.

8 **Water it.** Use water—not your feet!—to settle the soil. This will prevent over-packing, and allow the roots to "breathe." Watering is critical during the first few months, especially if you plant in spring. Water twice a week for the first month and once a week for the following two weeks. Be sure the root ball gets well watered, too, because the soil of the root

ball is different from the soil around it. This is critical until the roots have time to grow into the new soil.

9 **Mulch it.** Apply 2 to 4 inches of mulch over the prepared growing circle, except for an area 6 to 8 inches from the trunk of the tree. You may use bark, wood chips, old sawdust, leaf mold, or commercially prepared material for your mulch.

10 **Nurture it.** Use a commercially available biodegradable polypropylene shelter if you are planting seedlings or small trees 2 feet in height or shorter. These shelters will help establish and speed the growth of these small trees, which are less expensive than the larger trees (see illustration below). Larger trees don't need shelters. You may want to use a flexible stake to help support the tree when it is young (see illustration, page 58). The stake is for support only, not for training a bent tree. Don't use wire to hold the tree; if the wire isn't removed in time, it can kill the tree.

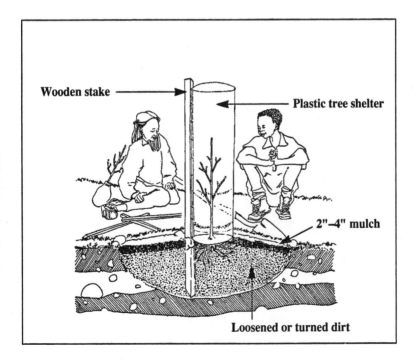

Aftercare

Watering, trimming, and mulching are the three most important care issues. Give the newly planted tree a thorough watering once a week; frequent sprinkling only wets the surface. (See "Water for Life," page 60.) Unless you have used a slow-release fertilizer, wait six months before applying any form of fertilizer to the soil, and then spread only 3 pounds per inch of tree diameter throughout the widest possible growing area of the root system.

Watch for insect and disease problems. Wilting leaves or branches, changes in leaf color, webs, and sticky material on the leaves are all signs of insect and disease problems. Check with your local cooperative extension service or a tree expert if you see these signs.

OF STREETS, PITS, AND POTS

Planting trees in the urban forest can be a challenging endeavor, especially along streets and within the harsh conditions of the city center. Following are some suggestions.

Planting on the Streets

In suburban areas, there is often a grassy strip between the curb and the sidewalk, which can be a good spot for planting. But be sure to check with your city or municipality for rules and restrictions regarding these areas, which are generally publicly owned. Often the city will be glad to allow you to plant there, but may have a list of trees from which you must choose. The process for street-side planting in these sidewalk strips is much the same as that for yard trees, only the growing area will more likely be a rectangle about 8 feet long by the available width.

Prepare the ground by turning over the soil in the planting area to the depth of the root ball, the width of the tree lawn, and 6 to 8 feet in length. As with yard trees, the root ball is set on solid ground in the center of the prepared soil. Also, make sure that the top of the root ball is level with the surface of the surrounding ground. Water as with yard trees, and mulch regularly. (Mulching will also help discourage weeds.)

In the Pits

Often, the only available space to plant trees to shade sidewalks in our urban centers is the small stretch of soil that is left uncovered by concrete every 20 or 30 feet between the curb and the sidewalk. Although these spaces are almost always under public ownership, more and more citizens' groups are helping to plant trees in them. Be sure to consult municipal agencies before planting, and always check with the local utility companies about buried wires and pipes. Trees will never reach the age or size in these "tree pits" as they will in tree-lawn or yard settings, but there have been new advances in planting techniques to ensure their best health under these challenging planting and growing conditions.

Size. The pit should be at least 30 square feet in area and at least 4 feet wide and 7 feet long. If the pit is smaller than this, it may be possible to improve the soil or conditions just under the sidewalk to cajole the roots to grow to other nearby areas of soil

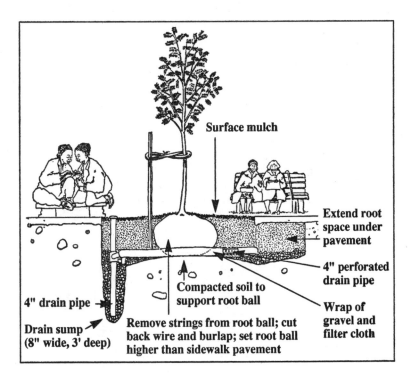

Surface mulch

Extend root space under pavement

4" perforated drain pipe

Compacted soil to support root ball

4" drain pipe

Drain sump (8" wide, 3' deep)

Remove strings from root ball; cut back wire and burlap; set root ball higher than sidewalk pavement

Wrap of gravel and filter cloth

within a 10-foot radius of the tree pit. Given the urgent need for healthy urban trees, it may also be possible to enlarge the pit by cutting into the sidewalk with concrete cutting equipment or digging some extra space underneath the sidewalk—but don't dig too much.

Drainage. Many pits are unsuitable for tree growth because the soil is too compacted to drain well. Perform the drainage test described on page 40 under "Wet or dry?"

Soil. Excavate all the soil in the pit to a depth of 2 to 2-1/2 feet. If drainage is moderate or poor, install an aeration ring and a drain sump. Return the soil to the pit, only adding amendments such as fertilizer and organic matter if the soil is particularly sandy. Test the soil for acidity (pH) to see if it is beyond the acceptable limits: between 3.5 and 8 on the pH scale. Water the soil as it enters the pit to settle it, and compact the soil in the center of the pit under the root ball to support it; newly planted trees that sink back into the soil will not flourish. Backfill and cover with 2 to 4 inches of mulch. If this area receives a lot of foot traffic, cover the pit with sand and bricks or pavers at the same level as the

Guy wire with protective covering

Wooden stake

adjoining sidewalk (although these pavers will reduce the tree's potential growth). Iron tree grates are not recommended.

Gone to Pot: Container Trees as a Last Resort

Street-side planting pots or containers are the most expensive way to plant street trees. Though it is always better to plant in the ground, there are many spaces deep in the urban jungle where soil is unsuitable or unavailable for planting but where greenery is desirable.

The cost is high for constructing a good container, but the cost of long-term maintenance far exceeds the cost of the pot. Along with engineering decisions involving the load-bearing capacity of the sidewalk, biological decisions about the size of the tree need to be considered. The volume of the soil will determine the ultimate tree size.

The container should be equipped with an irrigation system or a reservoir of water to eliminate the need for daily watering. Regular watering is imperative; if you skip one week of watering in midsummer, your tree will surely die.

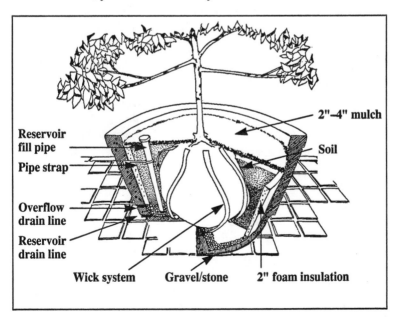

The oldest tree we've found in a container is a nineteen-year-old littleleaf linden that was watered faithfully three times a week every week of its life. Let there be no doubt: a containerized street tree is like a bonsai plant; it requires careful maintenance for long-term survival.

STEP FIVE: CARING FOR YOUR TREE

Trees are amazing examples of the adaptability and resilience of nature. They are also living, growing things and need the best conditions in order to thrive and provide you with their benefits for many years, even many generations, to come.

What Your New Tree Needs

Trees need three things to get a good start and live a long life: water, mulch, and pruning. Your lawn tree also needs protection from injury.

When cutting and weeding your lawn, take great care not to injure the delicate cambium layer just under the outer bark of your tree. Automatic weed cutters are especially dangerous to newly planted trees. The whirring plastic cutters on these weed whackers can bruise and wound young trees, allowing infections and microorganisms to invade and attack the tree's life-support systems. A better solution to weeding is to pull grass out by hand near the trunk of the tree, and keep the area mulched so weeds won't get started in the first place.

Water for Life

A newly planted tree needs adequate watering on a weekly basis. After that, it needs your assistance only in times of stress—during droughts and in midsummer heat. Trees show signs of needing water by dropping a percentage of leaves throughout the crown and losing the bright green color of their leaves. If water is abundant, tree growth can be improved by allowing trees extra water when the weather is hot and dry.

One good soaking is always worth more than a few casual sprinklings. Your tree's roots develop in response to how you water. Thorough watering produces healthy trees. An easy way to get water to the roots of your tree is to perforate a 5-gallon plastic bucket with several holes, place it about 2 feet from the trunk of the tree, and fill it to the top with water. The water will seep out of the holes slowly, allowing the tree's roots to get an adequate drink. Repeat this on the opposite side of the tree. How often you do this will depend, in large part, on the season, the size of your tree, and the climate in which you live. Once a week for a new tree in a moderate climate is a good rule of thumb.

You can also use a plastic soil soaker—an inexpensive garden-hose attachment that is perforated with tiny holes to let the water seep out slowly. Place it in a circular pattern around the tree, about 2 feet from the trunk. Water should be applied slowly so it does not run off but soaks deeply into the soil.

If you live in a drought-prone region where water is at a premium, you need to take care of larger, well-established trees on your property as well as the newly planted ones. During a drought, trees with large root systems need help, too, largely due to the poor quality of urban soils. Trees that have been planted near cement—in the middle of a patio, near a driveway or sidewalk, or in an office parking lot—are at particular risk during drought conditions. These trees have little access to surface moisture, and because water runs off the cement into the gutter instead of into their root zones, they often receive insufficient water even when it rains. These trees tend to rely on underground moisture, which is in short supply during a drought. You can help these large trees in at least four ways:

1 **Regular soaking.** Use the 5-gallon-bucket method described above, a soil soaker, or just a slow stream of water from a regular garden hose. The primary disadvantage to all of these methods is that wasteful runoff is likely if the tree is near a paved area or if the soil is compacted. If water does not percolate easily into the soil around the tree, use one of the following methods instead.

2 **Mulching.** Mulch prevents water from evaporating out of the soil and is a practical deterrent to drought (see below). Pull mulch away from the trunk to reduce damage from mice and insects.

3 **Deep-root irrigators.** This technique is useful for large trees, shrubs located on a slope, or clay soil. A deep-root irrigator is a pipe with holes that is inserted into the ground close to the root system. Water is injected into the ground under high pressure through a coupler at the top of the pipe.

4 **Vertical mulching.** This method of getting water to the roots is especially helpful for city trees in hard soil. First, use a soil auger to drill holes into the ground around the tree, being careful to drill far enough away from the trunk. Then fill the holes with gravel, loose soil, mulch, or special moisture-retaining materials such as corn fiber or synthetic polymers. This will allow air to reach the roots, and when you water the tree, the moisture will go where it will do the most good.

Mulch for Health

Mulch is almost anything you can put on top of the ground to slow down evaporation and prevent soil compaction and weed growth. Any organic material—leaves, bark, or wood chips—is good mulch, and compost is also excellent. Fortunately, anyone with a little outdoor space can make compost (see pages 64–65). Not only does making your own compost save money, it also gives you a perfect way to recycle almost all your yard waste and help keep those clippings out of our overcrowded landfills.

Prune for Health

After a couple of years, your tree will have grown enough to require some serious pruning to assist the tree's future growth. Pruning at a young age is one of the most important and least observed maintenance needs of a young tree. Branch growth can be directed by pruning small branches and snipping buds. Once branches grow, removing them leaves large wounds on the tree. And each pound of wood you remove from a tree because a branch is growing in the wrong direction could have been a pound of wood in a branch that shades your home or yard.

Unless you live in a particularly windy area, you should remove the stake after the tree's first season. Next comes the step that will assure your tree of a long and healthy life: trimming and pruning. Some conditions demand pruning, but others are more a matter of personal taste and aesthetics.

What to Prune

To keep your tree healthy and growing strong, you must prune all of the following:

☐ Dead or dying branches. They invite attack by insects and disease.

☐ Broken roots. Cut them off cleanly at the break and cover with soil.

☐ Crossed branches. Remove the one that has the least structural benefit to the tree's crown.

☐ Branches that form poor unions. Usually two branches that form a fork, or a tightly angled V, should be removed; they are not structurally sound and are likely to break off as the tree grows, causing severe damage to the tree.

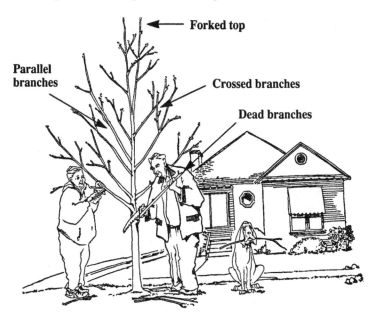

Making Your Own Compost

Composting involves little more than gathering organic material together to decompose. There are several recipes that claim to create the most nutritious compost and promote the fastest process of decomposition, yet they all depend on a few simple elements:

1 **Raw materials.** Compost can be manufactured from anything organic and, thus, biodegradable—leaves, grass clippings, paper, vegetable parings, leftover food, sawdust, wood ash, rock powder—you name it. But it is easier and more efficient if the larger elements for your compost pile are chopped or cut up first. For example, you may want to spread your raked leaves into a shallow pile, then shred them with a lawn mower. If inquisitive neighbors want to know why, exactly, you are "mowing" your leaves, tell them! It may give them the same idea. Meats, fat, and bones from the kitchen are not recommended—they decompose slowly and will probably smell and attract flies. Also, needles, bark, and wood chips from pine trees are highly acidic and should not be added to your compost pile unless you are making an acidic mulch for conifers.

2 **A container.** You can get by with nothing more than a basic pile of leaves, grass clippings, weeds, and sawdust thrown into a corner of your garden. Or you can choose to build a container which will speed up the process and make it more organized. Almost anything can be used to house the compost: a 55-gallon drum, chicken wire formed into a cylinder or square, brick or cinder-block bins, bales of hay, railroad ties, two-by-twos, four-by-fours, plywood—the choice is yours. Whatever kind of container you choose, make sure that it has plenty of air holes. While decomposition can occur without oxygen, such as in a pit, anaerobic decomposition takes much longer. The fastest composting process depends on available oxygen and lots of it. You also might consider making two bins: one for the composting, and the other to hold the finished product. The minimum size of a bin or pile to promote the process of decomposition is about 3 feet square and 3 feet high. Anything less doesn't provide the "critical mass" needed to allow the materials to heat up.

3 **A cover.** While it helps to keep the materials moist, use a cover to keep out the rain. A simple tarp is sufficient, but you can always get fancy and construct a small roof for your compost gazebo, if you like.

4 **A place in the sun.** Put the bin on well-drained, level ground. Not all neighbors appreciate a compost pile next to their patio, so keep it away from property lines. You may find the center of the garden is the best location, since all the materials are near at hand. Since the speed of the compost process depends on the heat that builds up within the pile, you should protect the compost from cooling winds as much as possible by placing it in the lee side of a bush or fence.

5 **A steady supply of materials.** Remember: decomposition needs air, so start with a layer of brush or cornstalk, then alternate layers, each a few inches thick, of high-nitrogen material, such as horse manure or grass clippings; garden soil; hay, straw, wood chips, or other such rough material; more clippings, sawdust, etc. Continue the cycle, keeping the pile covered, until it reaches about 5 feet in height. (For the chemically inclined, the carbon-to-nitrogen ratio for fastest decomposition should be about 25 to 1.) Moisten the layers with water if the materials are dry. Many people keep a small compost bucket in the kitchen where most organic materials—eggshells, coffee grounds, orange peels, etc.—are kept to be mixed into the compost pile.

6 **A few good turns.** A well-constructed pile will heat up in the center to about 130 degrees Fahrenheit within a few days, then cool off. Turn the pile about once a week, making sure that all the materials on the outside of the pile take their turn in the center. Your pile is fully composted when it fails to warm up after being turned. This could be as soon as three weeks, although it is safer to figure on a couple of months. Transfer the compost to the empty second container, and start a new pile in the first.

7 **A reason for being.** Once your compost is "cooked," it's ready to go to work. Don't expect it to look exactly like the bag of perfect potting soil you bought at the local gardening supply outlet, however. Homemade compost more closely resembles the mixture of rich leafy matter on the floor of a forest, a substance halfway between living matter and soil. You will soon learn to love it for its multiple uses: Dig your hard-earned compost into your garden plots. Use it to side-dress your rows of vegetables. Sift it through a colander for use as a seeding bed. Mix it with soil for potting plants. Suspend sacks of the stuff in water for nutritious "compost tea" to feed your plants. Help out your large trees by using it for vertical mulching. And, of course, spread it over the root systems of your trees, taking care to keep it 6 inches away from the trunks.

To Thin Out Smaller Trees: Pruning Shears

Just say "yes" to pruning shears and small pruning cuts. When a branch is small enough to cut with small hand pruners, excellent pruning decisions can be made which will maximize tree growth and minimize damage to the tree. And the person doing the pruning will learn a lot about tree growth by pruning small branches and helping the tree to grow in the most productive way possible.

On most yard trees, for example, you will want the lowest branches to be above your head. You can accomplish this in stages by pruning a little each year. Start with the lowest branches as soon as the trunk is large enough—after the tree has been in the ground for about a year. Each growing season thereafter, remove a couple of the lowest branches that grow straight out or at an upward angle from the trunk.

Removing many smaller branches throughout the crown is not a problem, but extra caution is important along the trunk. It's best to cut just before the growing season. Make sure the blade section of the shears cuts upward or sideways through the branch you are removing, and carefully target the location of the cut just outside the branch collar (see illustration on page 67). The cut should be made close to the trunk but not so close as to damage the branch-collar ridge. Use this same simple process to remove unwanted branches and laterals from other branches throughout the tree.

To Prune Larger Trees: Pruning Saws

Don't attempt to remove larger branches with pruning shears. You're likely to mash the branch and ruin your shears at the same time. And don't attempt to use a carpenter's saw either. It is designed to cut dry wood and will bind and get stuck cutting green branch-wood. Instead, use a pruning saw. Small pruning saws are not expensive and are designed to cut green wood.

Three Cuts to Perfection

Using a saw to remove a branch requires three separate cuts:

1 The first undercut is made about a foot from the final cut location and only a couple of inches into the branch.

2 The second cut, an inch farther out, goes right through the

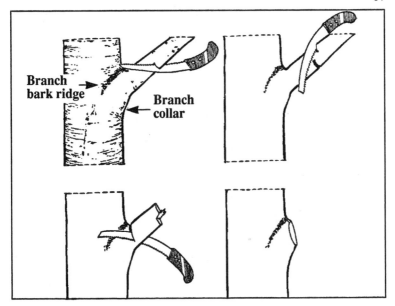

branch, removing the bulk of its weight and so preventing unwanted splitting.

[3] The final cut removes the short stub that remains, and is executed just beyond the branch collar. The branch collar is usually recognizable with a little practice. If you think of the branch as similar to a person's arm, the tree trunk or main branch from which the smaller branch emerges is the body. The branch collar is the shoulder. The branch itself narrows quickly, like an arm from a shoulder, after the branch collar.

Advice from a Pro

Spend a few moments each month surveying your trees. It can be an enjoyable pastime, and you can learn about your trees and keep them in good health just by looking and noticing changes. If you notice broken or dead limbs on small trees, you can probably tend to them yourself. If the trees are large, you should consult with a tree professional. You should also choose this option if you see significant changes in the color of the leaves in the middle of the growing season.

Choosing the best tree professional may take a little research. Generally, it is not wise to hire tree-care companies that solicit

Look Up! Trees, Poles, and Wires

The welter of wires that crisscross our cities belong to power, telephone, and cable companies. Each set of wires is governed by a different set of policies and regulations, but they all share a common concern: trees near the wires. Power lines are the primary concern because high-voltage electricity can jump to a nearby tree, causing sparks or a power outage. Pruning trees around power lines is especially dangerous. A person holding a metal pole or ladder that contacts a power line could be electrocuted. Children should never be allowed to play in trees that have grown near electrical cables.

Estimates show that the public spends about $3 million a day to cut tree branches away from suspended wires. Until all wires are placed underground, it makes sense to respect the presence of existing wires when planting. One way to do this is to plant a tree that will never reach the wires in the first place. Choose a slow-growing species that will not grow taller than 20 or 30 feet. Best of all, don't plant under wires at all.

business door-to-door. Keep in mind that some of your larger trees are worth several thousand dollars; it is safer to ensure your arboreal investment with a well-established professional company. Ask your neighbors for recommendations. If they can't give you a good referral, check with your local Arborists Association for their suggestions. In many areas, the International Society of Arboriculture certifies arborists and you can obtain a list from the organization's local chapter.

Arborists, like doctors, do differ on treatments for serious tree problems, so you may wish to get a second or even third opinion if your job is a large one. In large cities, consultants can be hired on an hourly basis. Often these are city foresters, electric utility foresters, and the like who perform consulting services after work hours. Many of these individuals are listed with the American Society of Consulting Arborists.

Beware of "tree doctors" who would use spikes to climb your

Taller majestic trees can co-exist with aerial wires if certain precautions are taken. Some trees can be directionally trimmed to grow on either side of the lines. Creative forms of pruning, such as cutting large branches off at a branch union (a method called "drop-crotch pruning"), can control the size of a tree's canopy. Pruning for specific purposes, such as avoiding wires, should only be done by a professional tree trimmer. This is very dangerous work, and an amateur can also damage the tree. It was once common practice for trimmers to top trees and stub off larger branches for line clearance, leaving trees looking like hat racks. This both wounded the trees and promoted prolific sprouting. Not only was this new growth weakly attached to the freshly cut limb, it also proceeded to grow very quickly right back to the wires. Using better pruning methods, today's knowledgeable tree experts cut branches at natural branching points, protecting the health of the tree and improving its shape.

live trees; they are quacks. Ask about this practice before any work begins. If they say "yes" to spikes, say "no" to them. Topping (reducing the height of a tree by cutting the top portion off, also known as "pollarding" or "hatracking") is also a questionable practice and is only recommended when the tree has already suffered serious damage, such as from high winds or a plane crash. Reject companies that recommend topping. Like a good hairstylist, a good arborist can remove up to 50 percent of a tree's wood in such a way that you would never notice the difference once the leaves grow in.

Request a copy of a company's certificates of insurance and workers' compensation before you allow anyone to work on your property. Phone the insurance company and state agency to make sure that the company is still covered and protected for damage to your house and injury to its workers. Uninsured workers can sue you, the homeowner, for compensation.

Always request a written estimate of the work to be performed with all materials to be used and all individual tasks and their costs clearly laid out. Never pay in advance, and don't pay until all the work (and any necessary corrections) have been performed to your or your consultant's satisfaction.

If you get the work done in the off-season, you can secure lower winter rates. And if you and several of your neighbors join together for group tree-care, you can obtain additional savings.

STEP SIX: ENJOYING THE FRUITS OF YOUR LABOR

If you choose your tree intelligently, plant it with care, and nurture it properly, your cooperation with nature is sure to bring you pleasure—along with the benefits of increased property value and decreased energy bills—for many years to come. By example you will have already become an advocate for the urban forest in your neighborhood and community at large. In the next chapter, we will explore more ways in which you can contribute to your city's urban forest.

THE ANATOMY OF A TREE

In order to take the best care possible of your valuable tree and assure a long life for it, you need to know something about its structure and system of growth. Living in the city, an urban forest tree is already at a disadvantage. The more knowledgeable you become about what your tree needs, the better chance it has.

The Three Worlds of the Tree

Underground. Many people think that the full profile of a tree resembles an exercise dumbbell, with the roots extending as far below the ground as the canopy does above. In fact, a wine glass set on a dinner plate more closely represents the real structure of a tree. The bulk of the tree's root system spreads out in a fairly flat pattern within the top 3 feet of the surface of the ground, with the majority of the roots within the top foot.

Roots extend out from the trunk at the root collar, a bulge often found at the ground line. From four to eleven woody roots start here and grow horizontally through the soil. As these major roots—known as transport roots—grow away from the trunk, they decrease in diameter and spread out, under ideal conditions, covering an area ten to fifteen times that of the diameter of the tree's canopy. It is the transport roots that support the tree.

The feeder roots grow upward from the transport roots in a complex web that forms a mat or fan, ending in a filigree of thousands of fine fibrous roots. A mature tree can have hundreds of miles of roots, and most of the length is in the fibrous mats where the largest roots are only as thick as pencil lead. With the help of symbiotic fungi, called mycorrhizae, trees are able to absorb minerals from the soil along with water. By far, the bulk of a tree's ground-based nutrition comes from the loose and easily accessible surface layers of the soil where air and organic matter are easily available. But these upper layers are also vulnerable, and the feeder root system is susceptible to changes in growing

The shape of a tree resembles a wine glass set on a plate.

conditions, especially drought. Under stress, the tiny feeder roots may die, but they grow back quickly. In fact, recent research has demonstrated that there is more dying and regeneration of the roots than any of the tree's other systems, including the leaves.

It is important to understand that roots have no "feelers" or sensors of any kind and do not grow *toward* anything. They simply send out feeder roots which may or may not encounter what they need for survival. If the roots are lucky enough to grow where moisture and air are plentiful, they will live and provide sustenance to the tree; if not, they simply wither and die.

Tree roots thrive only in loose, well-drained soils with adequate nutrition and, especially, oxygen. Roots will not grow well in highly compacted soil, which describes most city soils, although they will grow down cracks and along sewer lines, where moisture is more plentiful. City soil, which is often highly compacted and therefore severely lacking in oxygen, inhibits root growth and

URBAN ROOT SYSTEM

Urban soils are dense and compacted, containing very little air space. Urban trees are also overexposed to sun and wind. For these reasons and others, the root systems of city trees are shallow and sparse.

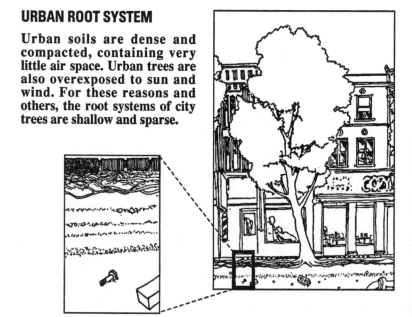

shortens a tree's life. That is why simply digging a hole in city soil and dropping the tree into it is really dooming the tree to a shortened life span, since the roots will never be able to penetrate beyond the original excavation. Ideal soil is 50 percent air, so heavy pedestrian use, nearby vehicular traffic, or the passage of heavy machinery can compact soil around a tree and do immense damage to a tree by cutting off the roots' access to oxygen.

Since so much of the root system is just under the surface, trees are also exposed to the dangers of many herbicides and, of course, the chemical insults of dog urine. And because the root systems of large trees can extend farther than 60 feet radially, whatever chemicals your neighbors put on their lawns may influence your tree's health. Trees are attacked by herbicides designed to eradicate broad-leafed weeds. Dicamba (Benvel), Trimek, and glyphosate (Roundup) herbicides can kill some trees and distort the leaves of others. Rock salt used for de-icing, lime

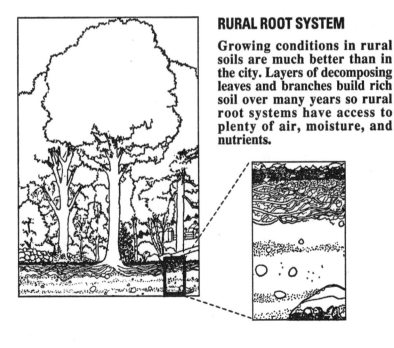

RURAL ROOT SYSTEM

Growing conditions in rural soils are much better than in the city. Layers of decomposing leaves and branches build rich soil over many years so rural root systems have access to plenty of air, moisture, and nutrients.

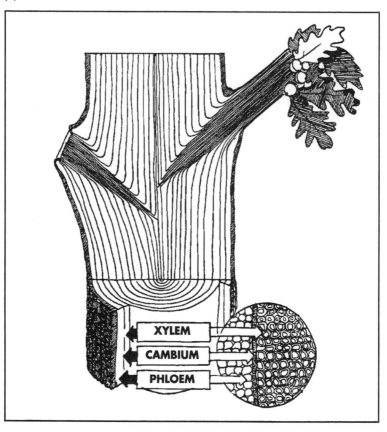

from concrete, and even cleaning solvents and oil can all damage a tree's vulnerable root system.

In the trunk. The roots gather the water and nutrients that the tree needs to survive. The trunk is the arterial system—like our arteries and veins—that transports these materials to the leaves in the outer layers of the tree trunk and inner layers of the bark. Just beneath the bark is the cambium, the "cell factory" of the tree. Cells that form outward from the cambium layer develop into the phloem (the layer of tissue which transports the food up and down the trunk) and the bark. Cells that form inward from the cambium become xylem, or sapwood, which conducts the water up and down the trunk.

As the tree grows outward, older xylem stops its transport function and becomes heartwood. In some cases, this heartwood may actually rot away completely, leaving a perfectly healthy hollow tree with only the living outer rings performing all the necessary vital functions of the trunk. It is here, in the outer layers of wood, that in a large tree hundreds of gallons of water and nutrients are sucked up from the roots, and tons of sugar-laden sap are pushed down from the leaves in a pumplike action. This massive flow of fluids makes the tree the largest vascular creation on the planet.

A tree grows upward much like adding an ice cream cone to an existing stack of other cones. This means that a branch that grows out of the trunk at a height of, say, 4 feet from the ground will certainly grow in diameter, as will the trunk itself, but the branch will remain the same distance from the ground for the duration of the tree's life.

The same goes for injuries—whether initials carved on a tree trunk or slashes from a mower. Trees overcome injuries and fight off infections by sealing off the affected part. Whether wounded by a badly pruned branch or the attack of a bark beetle, a tree will carry its scars for the rest of its life.

The changing story of leaves. The biological engine that drives a tree's myriad mechanisms is found in the microscopic chloroplasts—units of chlorophyll—found within leaves. Here the energy from sunlight is used to transform carbon dioxide, water, and inorganic salts (from the tree's roots) into complex organic materials, most important, carbohydrates in the form of sugars. Water, oxygen, and traces of other gases are released as by-products of photosynthesis.

Under good conditions, the leaves use some of the sugar they have manufactured to power their own organic factory and pump the surplus back down the phloem, feeding the tree's processes of growth and healing. Photosynthesis is the basis of all life on the planet, and is the only organic process that pulls carbon dioxide from the atmosphere and "fixes" it in the form of sugars and, eventually, wood. This process takes place one molecule at a time, but given the number of leaves in a large tree and the total surface area involved, the amount of carbon dioxide absorbed by each tree soon rises to several pounds a year.

Overlooked Gems of the Urban Forest

Many nurseries sell trees that are often easy for growers to propagate but may not always be the best for survivability or long-term benefits as members of the urban forest. Below is a short list of some species that are considered exotic or have been overlooked. If the trees that interest you are not available at your local nursery, ask for them. Your requests will help make these species more available. You may need to order some of the following types of trees from mail-order houses (see Resources).

NORTHEAST
Connecticut, Maine, Massachusetts, New Hampshire, New York, New Jersey, Pennsylvania, Rhode Island, Vermont:

- **Turkish hazel *(Corylus colurna)***
  This tree is rarely plagued by insects or disease and grows well throughout the northeast and into the plains states. It is also a favorite for wildlife.
- **willow oak *(Quercus phellos)***
  Most often found in the south, this species can also grow well in the north. But make sure your tree was grown from local seeds. The autumn color display of yellow, brown, and russet makes this tree worth the work and the wait.

MID-ATLANTIC
Delaware, Maryland, North Carolina, South Carolina, Virginia, West Virginia:

- **lacebark elm or Chinese elm *(Ulmus parvifolia)***
  Don't confuse this with the Siberian elm, which is often mistakenly sold in nurseries as the Chinese elm. The lacebark elm supplies a dense shade and is resistant to many of the ailments that afflict fellow members of its species, including Dutch elm disease.
- **Japanese flowering apricot *(Prunus mume)***
  This tree flowers in the off-season—as early as January—and so makes

an excellent screen tree, as effective as the popular leyland cypress when planted on the borders of your yard.

SOUTHEAST
Alabama, Arkansas, Florida, Georgia, Kentucky, Louisiana, Mississippi, Tennessee:

Preferred species here are drought tolerant—meaning they can survive with available rainfall only—but even drought-tolerant trees need a little help in the first years of life. Water these trees regularly the spring after planting so the root system can get properly established.

- **bald cypress *(Taxodium distichum)***
  This pyramid-shaped tree, which can grow to 100 feet tall (keep clear of overhead wires!) is an attractive conifer that also loses its delicate and feathery sprays of leaves in the winter (i.e., it becomes "bald"). This tree can withstand hurricane-force winds, an important consideration in this part of the country.

MIDWEST
Illinois, Indiana, Iowa, Michigan, Minnesota, Missouri, Ohio, Wisconsin:

- **Kentucky coffeetree *(Gymnocladus dioicus)***
  This hardy and adaptable tree has an unusual fruit—a leathery pod 5 to 10 inches long—which early settlers roasted as a coffee substitute. (Children should be warned not to eat the sticky gum of this seed pod, as it can cause stomach upset.)

WESTERN INTERIOR
Colorado, Idaho, Kansas, Oklahoma, Montana, Nebraska, Nevada, North Dakota, South Dakota, Utah, Wyoming:

- **bur oak *(Quercus macrocarpus)***
  A drought-tolerant native of the southwest, this tree can tolerate the searing sun, and its leaves remain a deep green at the height of summer.
- **hackberry *(Celtis occidentalis)***
  This is a relatively fast-growing tree that does well in a variety of soils and can withstand the temperature extremes that characterize this part of the country. The hackberry also produces an abundance of orange-red fruit that ripen in the fall and attract birds and wildlife.

(continued)

SOUTHWEST
Arizona, New Mexico, Texas:

- **bur oak** *(see Western Interior, page 77)*
- **desert willow** *(Chilopsis linearis)*
  This small tree (about 25 feet high when fully grown) has graceful, drooping branches and, as its name suggests, can get by with little water once established.

PACIFIC NORTHWEST
Oregon, Washington:

- **handkerchief (dove) tree** *(Davidia involucrata)*
  This species resembles any other green-leafed tree for most of the year; but in May, it is transformed into a creature of rare beauty when two white bracts (a leaflike part of the flower) hang from each large blossom, giving the appearance that hundreds of white handkerchiefs (or doves) are resting in the tree's foliage.
- **Japanese snowbell** *(Styrax japonicus)*
  A small tree with strong horizontal branches, this species supplies good fall color. When its fragrant white blossoms appear in June, this tree offers what appear to be parallel green-and-white tiers of color, as the leaves angle up and the flowers angle down. (This tree needs abundant water and well-drained soil.)

CALIFORNIA

- **Chinese tallow tree** *(Sapium sebiferum)*
  This small, uniformly shaped, deciduous tree provides a mixture of purple, yellow, and orange color in the fall. It is able to tolerate most soils, although it prefers the slightly acidic kind. It is an excellent lawn and street tree.
- **Brisbane box** *(Tristania conferta)*
  This evergreen tree, a moderate- to quick-growing species, reaches a maximum height of 30 to 60 feet. It needs water in its early years, but is drought tolerant once the roots are established. Creamy white flowers bloom in summer months, and it also has an attractive reddish-brown, naturally shedding bark.

PART III:

GLOBAL RELEAF, THE COMMUNITY, AND THE WORLD

KEEPING THE GLOBAL PICTURE IN MIND

Ever since the astronauts returned with pictures of the Earth as a single blue-green globe wreathed in streams of white clouds, we human beings were able, at long last, to see that we all live on the fragile surface of a single planet. Yet it is clear that as we move toward a new century, our shared home is now facing environmental problems of unprecedented proportions.

We now know that the ozone layer, which protects us from harmful solar radiation, is slowly being depleted. And the amount of carbon dioxide in the atmosphere, which boosts the greenhouse effect, appears to be altering our climate. These are changes of planetary proportions, and they will have an impact on everyone who lives on the surface of the Earth in the future, regardless of nationality. The Cold War has been replaced by the "Warming War."

The seemingly overwhelming problems we face are a direct result of industrial development—actions of individuals taken step by step, factory by factory, and automobile by automobile over the last two centuries of modern history. But if people and their commercial enterprise were responsible for our present environmental distress, then people and their actions are also the key to healing it. In the past, we have been destroyers. How quickly can we shift our attitudes and put the same enterprise and energy into being creative problem solvers? The answer lies in our willingness—individually and collectively—to take the first step now.

A Challenge for the Future

In 1988, the American Forestry Association realized that in order to come to grips with the challenge of our environmental situation, especially in regard to global warming, a bold new form of action was required. In order to reach as many people as possible, the organization instituted a program called Global ReLeaf. In keeping with its 115-year-old history as the oldest citizen-conservation organization in the nation, the American Forestry Association's emphasis in this massive environmental repair program begins—but does not end—with trees.

Forests are a major factor in the planet's well-being, and Global ReLeaf has a variety of approaches to address the many roles that trees play in our environment. For one, it recognizes the importance of promoting policies that will save the tropical rainforests, the very "lungs of the planet," where 50 million acres of land are cleared each year, 80 percent by large-scale slash-and-burn for agriculture, and 20 percent by logging. Global ReLeaf also considers it crucial for America to rethink its domestic forest policies to create more and healthier forests and protect the dwindling old-growth ecosystems that remain. But since the majority of the American population live in urban centers—90 percent by the year 2000—and because city trees can play a critical role in reducing atmospheric carbon dioxide, the focus of Global ReLeaf that strikes home for most of us is the program's emphasis on urban forestry.

MAKING A DIFFERENCE AT HOME AND ABROAD

Planting a single tree and caring for it as it grows is one of the most positive actions a city dweller can take toward creating a better future. It is an empowering act, one that allows us to think globally while acting locally. And it is a clear example of the

Trees, Hydrocarbons, and Air Pollution

Trees are famous for their ecological benefits. Recently, however, stories have been appearing in our newspapers, suggesting that trees actually contribute to pollution. The question is: if trees and other green plants produce oxygen and capture carbon in the air, can they pollute the air as well?

The answer lies in looking at the "big picture" of urban ecology. All growing plants, including trees, emit a variety of gases. These include hydrocarbons in varying degrees, depending on species. Hydrocarbons are part of the natural chemistry of the Earth's atmosphere. The problem is that by burning fossil fuels for our vehicles and factories, we are putting far too many pollutants into the atmospheric chemical stew. Estimates show that industrial production, trucks, and cars produce 88 percent of all the hydrocarbons entering the atmosphere each year. Under the powerful rays of the sun, these pollutants produce a variety of other harmful chemicals as well, including ozone and smog, which are formed when sunlight reacts with hydrocarbons and nitrogen oxides. Heat speeds up these reactions. Not surprisingly, the areas of greatest pollution are our cities, where cars and factories are concentrated on urban heat islands.

central message of Global ReLeaf that something can be done by concerned citizens who want to reverse the trends of forest depletion and environmental damage, and promote new trends to help build a healthier environmental future.

You may plant and care for only one tree, but that single act of commitment links you to a movement that stretches across borders and over continents. People around the globe are just as concerned about the environment as you are, and they, too, are choosing to solve our shared problems one small step at a time.

Local programs across the United States have resulted in millions of trees being planted in small towns and large cities, by individuals, organizations, scout groups, and neighborhood

The Environmental Protection Agency (EPA), under the Clean Air Act, has been working for almost two decades to solve this problem. EPA scientists traditionally assumed that natural hydrocarbons—such as those emitted by trees—were relatively unimportant in the smog equation, so they focused their attention and resources on reducing hydrocarbon emissions from automobiles and factories. But urban smog levels remained too high. Research showed that unless nitrogen oxides were also controlled, the necessary airborne components of smog would still be present—due, in part, to the natural hydrocarbons produced by trees and other plants.

Does this mean we should plant fewer trees to combat smog? Quite the opposite. Because trees have a powerful effect on cooling our urban heat islands, they have a most important role to play in smog reduction. What we really need to control is the overload of people-produced pollution—especially nitrogen oxides. More people and more industry will inevitably produce more polluting compounds, and cities will remain our most polluted places. Therefore, if we can plant trees in places and in sufficient numbers to be most effective in cooling city buildings and sheltering them in the winter—reducing the need for energy—we will be contributing to smog reduction. And while we're working to reduce pollution of all types, we should choose our species carefully, too. If we have choices between varieties of trees that tend to produce high levels of hydrocarbons and equally adapted species that produce lower levels, we should opt for the latter whenever possible. Watch for more information on which trees in your area produce the least hydrocarbons as further research data become available.

associations. Corporate Global ReLeaf campaigns now number nearly 100 and are growing by several each month. Twenty-five states and more than 500 cities have established official Global ReLeaf campaigns, often supported by significant public and private funds. Thousands of individual community projects have been initiated nationwide, and similar activities are underway all around the world.

The Global Connection

Within months of the launch of Global ReLeaf, a Canadian branch was formed, and campaigns began to blossom throughout Europe. Global ReLeaf was featured on the Voice of

America, and after the Berlin Wall fell, requests for information poured in by the hundreds from Eastern Europe. Even more recently, interest has been expressed by organizations in the Czechoslovakian republics, Lithuania, Bulgaria, and Ukraine. In Hungary, programs under the auspices of Global ReLeaf have already produced results, with new groves along the Danube and new trees on the streets of Budapest. Young trees—nurtured and cared for in backyards, streets, schoolyards, and reforested fields around the world—now bear witness to the power of citizens who decided to make a difference. In years to come, as these tall and noble trees stand proudly against the clear sky, they will be remembered as living mementos of the first wave of citizen action in the revolution that turned the tide on global pollution.

The American Forestry Association is currently seeking international partners, nonprofit organizations from other nations that are willing and able to put the Global ReLeaf program concept to work in their countries. As an education and action campaign, Global ReLeaf has been successfully "translated" into many national programs, including those in Austria, Costa Rica, Ecuador, Germany, Spain, and the United Kingdom. Each Global ReLeaf International Partner designs a program that best fits the needs of its own country.

The Greening of the Executive Branch

After years of highly visible Global ReLeaf activities, buttressed by a growing public awareness of environmental issues, the White House responded on a national scale. New federal programs support aggressive urban and community forestry projects. The 1990 Farm Bill included new programs encouraging conversion of marginal crop and pasture land to trees, as well as emphasizing the planting and nurturing of windbreaks, shelterbelts, and stream-corridor buffers. And President Bush recognized the importance of trees in his 1990 State of the Union address in which he challenged Americans to plant an extra one billion trees per year as part of the new "America the Beautiful" program.

Lowcountry ReLeaf

In 1989, when some folks in Charleston, South Carolina, set a date to establish a tree-planting organization in their area, they didn't realize how necessary such a group was going to be. Six days before the initial meeting was to take place, Hurricane Hugo tore through the state and devastated many of the trees. Then, more than ever, there was a dire need for urban forestry recovery efforts, and Lowcountry ReLeaf was off and running.

Thirty-five tree plantings were held on Arbor Day, kicking off the urban reforestation effort in the tri-county area of Berkeley, Charleston, and Dorchester. The group's main goal at the time was to keep up the momentum. Since then, Lowcountry ReLeaf has far surpassed its goal, involving thousands of citizens in planting thousands of trees. Lowcountry ReLeaf accepts funding applications for trees from local governments, schools, churches, and neighborhood associations. The applicants must attend an educational seminar on site and tree selection and preparation, planting, and maintenance. In order to be accepted for sponsorship, applicants must develop a plan showing their commitment to using appropriate trees, planting techniques, and tree care. Lowcountry ReLeaf's standards are so high that every tree-planting season, some applicants are unable to meet the requirements.

Applicants that do receive support are assigned a volunteer project coordinator, who is responsible for on-site analysis, assisting with project development, helping determine which trees are best suited for the area, and overseeing planting and follow-up. "I'm proud to say that our tree survival rate is incredibly good because we do take the time to really educate people on the value and maintenance of trees," says Lydia Evans, the organization's executive director and sole staffer. The projects, which range from planting one tree on school grounds to 150 trees in a large park, are predominantly funded by corporate and individual contributions at various events. For example, WCIV Channel 4 in Charleston organized a shrub sale with the help of Winn-Dixie stores and a $20,000 donation of holly and juniper shrubs from Carolina Nurseries. Channel 4 produced its own television spots using local celebrities to promote the event. As a result of this effort, $35,000 was raised for the organization.

Famous and Historic Trees

Since before Columbus landed on the shores of the New World, trees have served as sentinels, watching over all who lived here. Rooted in America's past, historic trees have witnessed the events that shaped our country. These special trees have stood over the stirring orations of Abraham Lincoln, felt the pierce of bullets at Shiloh, and were warmed by the campfires of the first settlers. Every tree has a story to tell.

The American Forestry Association's Famous and Historic Trees program gives individuals and groups across the country the opportunity to plant and care for the descendants of the very trees that stood at the crossroads of our nation's history or were owned or planted by famous people. Trees are researched and authenticated as to their lineage, seeds are collected, and small trees are carefully tended until they are a suitable size for planting. These unique, container-grown specimens are then ready to be shipped directly to you. Hundreds of trees are available and are recommended based on supplies and suitable species for your climatic conditions. They include trees such as:

- Mount Vernon Red Maple
- Admiral Chester Nimitz White Oak
- Helen Keller Water Oak
- Columbus White Oak
- Washington, D.C. Tidal Basin Japanese Cherry Tree
- Dr. Martin Luther King, Jr., Laurel Oak
- Gettysburg Sycamore
- Nathan Hale Green Ash
- Edgar Allan Poe Hackberry
- John Paul Jones Paper Birch
- Wright Brothers Sweet Gum
- Betsy Ross American Sycamore

A Winning Strategy

We may win a few battles against environmental degradation by planting trees in a park in Manhattan, protecting Chesapeake Bay in Maryland with shoreline forests, and using shade trees for energy conservation in Tucson. But in order to win the war against pollution, we need to improve every park, defend every bay, and shade every city. And that will take widespread awareness, effective planning, and commitment by many people working in their own communities to bring about change.

Currently, the tree canopies of America's cities cover about

Acknowledged by a personalized "Certificate of Authenticity," these trees will become family heirlooms and treasured community groves. They also make wonderful gifts and can spark an appreciation of history as well as nature.

You can participate in the Famous and Historic Tree program through any of the following projects:

- **Individual Plantings.** A limited number of Famous and Historic Trees are available for home planting. They include the Mount Vernon Red Maple, grown from the seeds of trees at George Washington's famous estate; and the Walden Woods Red Maple from the very site made famous by Henry David Thoreau.
- **Historic Groves.** Community organizations, businesses, civic and educational groups, or private individuals can sponsor Historic Groves of twenty or more trees. These groves will be a long-term educational and environmental resource for the community in schools, parks, and neighborhoods. They can also be used as fund-raising projects.
- **America's Historic Forest.** Corporations, groups, and individuals can actively plant trees in America's Historic Forest, a 1,500-acre historical and environmental theme park near Des Moines, Iowa.

Every tree planted not only helps the Earth but also helps to educate future generations of Americans in history and the environment. And a major portion of the proceeds from the sale of each tree goes to the Global ReLeaf Fund to support community tree-planting and tree-care projects.

To learn more about the Famous and Historic Trees program and how you or your group can get involved, call 1-800-677-0727.

30 percent of the urban surface area. One goal of Global ReLeaf is to double that figure. Cooling our urban heat islands with trees will require millions of people who are willing to plant and care for millions of city trees in the years to come.

Homeowners play an important role in this scenario. As we discussed in Part I, using trees to shade individual houses will result in reduced cooling and heating costs and lower emissions of carbon dioxide from power plants. But everyone who lives in the city—homeowners and apartment and condominium dwellers alike—has a role to play in growing greener cities through Global ReLeaf.

The Decade of the Citizen-Activist

Planting trees is only the first step. Global ReLeaf also means a commitment to caring for trees, nurturing the young whips, and pruning the trees, making sure that they reach maturity and survive as long as possible. This means involving citizens in a lifetime of action with trees and the environment. Ultimately, Global ReLeaf is much more about commitment to our cities and the environment as a whole, and less about the number of trees that are planted. The crucial element in this equation is the role of the concerned citizen.

Enthusiastic citizens can organize to plant trees on city streets, in parking lots, in parks, in abandoned lots, and on barren rights-of-way. Concerned individuals can get together to care for young street trees and find ways to support their local tree-care program. They can raise the awareness of elected officials to increase the local budgets for tree planting and municipal tree care. Educators and parents can teach children to appreciate the benefits of trees and introduce them to the dynamics of the environment. Global ReLeaf may begin with planting trees, but it extends into a wide-ranging network of commitment to environmental education and community action.

THE COMMUNITY CONNECTION

All projects to develop the urban forest, whether planting a few dozen or a few thousand trees, developing curriculum material, or establishing a tree-care operation, require three basic elements: organization, planning, and funding. These are all challenging, often frustrating enterprises—but fortunately, planting trees is a very popular activity, one that puts people in touch with nature. Once you make the decision to organize a community tree planting, Global ReLeaf is close at hand, backing you and your group at every step with resource material and advice. The rewards you will receive for your activism are powerful: the satisfaction of helping others to improve your community now and contribute to the health of the environment for generations to come.

Organizing a community group to plant and care for the urban forest—whether it's as small as your scout troop or as large as an international corporation—is a hands-on labor of love for people who share a common vision and a common pride in accomplishment. In a more immediate sense, it is also a great way to meet and work with like-minded people in an endeavor that will make community pride last for generations.

The Citywide Survey

Until you really know the condition of your urban forest and the state of the environment in which it exists, you cannot take appropriate action to improve either one. An urban forest grows, dies, and changes every day. The goal of your committee is, first, to have it grow faster than it dies and, second, to determine what its potential is and help guide it to that level. A citywide urban forest survey is the place to start. The survey will disclose your community's most pressing environmental needs and supply the

City Trees at Risk

This is a critical time in the history of America's urban forests. Tree planting is a widespread and popular activity, and never before have there been so many vigorous and enthusiastic citizen groups actively involved in planting and caring for city trees and teaching the benefits of urban forestry. Yet, in spite of all this citizen interest, our nation's urban forests are dwindling at an alarming rate.

A survey of twenty major cities from Seattle to Washington, D.C., and from Boston to Atlanta, completed by the American Forestry Association in 1991, reveals just how serious and extensive the situation is for the trees on our city streets:

- More street trees die than are planted each year.
- An average of 70 percent of our cities with tree-maintenance programs have cut them back.
- Almost half (45 percent) of the cities surveyed do not have routine street-tree maintenance programs at all.
- More than 50 percent of the tree-planting spaces along city streets are

Average Life of Street Trees
Species Commonly Grown in Communities
(averaged over a ten-year period)

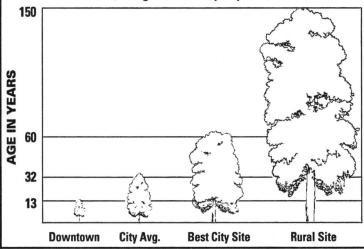

empty, and that percentage is expected to increase in coming years.

- In the twenty cities surveyed, the average life span of a downtown street tree was only thirteen years.
- About 75 percent of the cities do not regularly survey the condition of their urban forest.
- Dead and dying trees are backlogged for removal in 80 percent of our cities.

"These budget cuts that are now killing tree programs are really killing trees," says Neil Sampson, executive vice president of the American Forestry Association and creator of its Global ReLeaf campaign. "But the real losers are city residents who will breathe more polluted air, find their overly hot cities becoming even hotter, and who will pay more to cool their homes and businesses."

The good news is that citizen groups are active in every city surveyed and are becoming increasingly successful in attracting the support of local and national businesses for their efforts. What is needed now is for citizen groups to show more support for city tree professionals and their programs. So, when you join one of the tree-planting groups in your area, or form one of your own, don't forget to include the city forester in your plans—and if there isn't a tree program in your city, demand one! Working together, we can make a difference.

City Tree-Planting Levels
A Call to Action

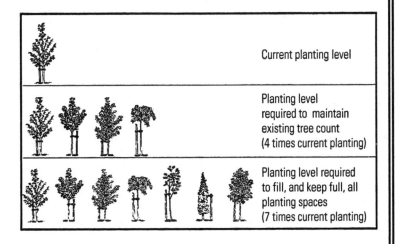

	Current planting level
	Planting level required to maintain existing tree count (4 times current planting)
	Planting level required to fill, and keep full, all planting spaces (7 times current planting)

necessary leverage to pry loose public funds to see that the community's goals are met.

After you have assembled a dedicated core of volunteers, you will need the participation of a professional tree-person with the expertise to train the volunteers to identify and measure trees in public areas. The best source of this help locally will be your city forester or arborist. Check with your local parks and recreation or public works department. Excellent technical assistance is also available from your county extension service agent or your local state forestry agency office. Your survey team will also have to rate the condition of the city's trees, which can be done under the supervision of the trained experts on your team. If the area to be examined is too large for the number of volunteers, a representative sample can be surveyed and an estimate made of the condition of the urban forest at large.

The survey, once completed and analyzed, yields a wealth of information, including the overall condition and value of the urban forest and the location of likely planting sites. Once this step has been completed, your group can speak with some authority about the trees and start making estimates of the cost of planting and caring for trees throughout the community. The survey exercise will help you see the urban forest and the changes that it undergoes on a daily, weekly, and yearly basis.

Once the fieldwork is done, some paperwork must start, beginning with writing a report for your neighbors, elected representatives, and newspaper and television reporters. People will want to know why they should be interested in the trees, and many will think in terms of finances, especially your community leaders. You will have to think in terms of cost and benefits when you speak to the decision makers. You may have to put together a variety of different contingency budgets, from one that covers the costs of a bare-bones maintenance program (removing dead trees, for example), through an annual trimming and maintenance budget, to a bold new planting program and upgraded maintenance cycle. Gather public support for the report by speaking to several local groups, elected officials, and the media.

Trees for Tucson, Global ReLeaf

After reading about the American Forestry Association's Global ReLeaf program in 1989, Joan Lionetti of Tucson, Arizona, wanted to start a major tree-planting effort in her community. First, she put together a list of approximately fifty community leaders who could generate support. Then she developed a detailed agenda and planned a meeting with the objective that "people would come out of it with a commitment to the program." Her strategy worked. Everyone who was invited attended, and all the original members have remained with the organization, which was dubbed "Trees for Tucson." The immediate support that Lionetti was able to round up, plus the 12,000 volunteers who have jumped on the band wagon, have made the program a model of grassroots success.

Lionetti established eight separate committees with clearly defined goals and tasks. The Tree Selection Committee spent more than 400 volunteer hours compiling an official tree list of fifty-four desert-adapted trees. Gaining the cooperation of the city's parks and recreation department and the city streets and transportation department, Trees for Tucson established a checklist of city requirements for planting in public rights-of-way. Reducing red tape has enabled people to focus on the task at hand—planting trees.

Trees for Tucson also stresses aftercare, especially the watering of trees. This is very important in the desert where rains come and go quickly. Because flash floods were a problem, the organization developed a technique called rainwater harvesting. Swales (shallow trenches that follow the contour of the land) are cut to trap and divert rainwater, and the water is used to irrigate planted areas. Trees for Tucson incorporated this simple but remarkable technique into a revegetation project at Freedom Park in June 1991. A strip of natural desert in the city was targeted as a garbage-transfer station and the land was bladed down. Nevertheless, the neighborhood association successfully fought the creation of the station. At about the same time, Trees for Tucson's Neighborhood Committee needed a place to demonstrate the new water harvesting/revegetation technique. It was a perfect match. The city, Freedom Park Neighborhood Association, and Trees for Tucson worked together to bring the land back to life.

EIGHT STEPS TO ORGANIZING A COMMUNITY

① SETTING GOALS, FINDING SITES

You know and understand the importance of trees. What exactly do you want to accomplish by planting them in a particular place? What is your specific goal?

Starting Small

To assure success, start with a project of modest proportions. The urban forest is everywhere in the city, no less on private property than on city-owned areas. Consider gathering together several of your neighbors for a large-scale tree-planting weekend. If you choose this route, you can share the physical labor and costs, as well as the equipment and materials—your neighbor's pickup truck, the rented rototiller, even the peat moss. If you've ever been involved in organizing a joint garage sale, church

bazaar, or block party, you can organize a group to plant and care for a group of trees (and have a party, too!).

Hitting the Streets

If your vision for trees is wider than your immediate neighborhood, then your range is virtually unlimited. Since resources are often limited, selecting the best places for planting is critical. In more established areas, street trees are always in need of care and, very often, replacement. You may choose to plant energy-conserving trees in local schoolyards or to shade parking lots; or you may decide to put in a whole mini-forest along a treeless right-of-way.

Fixing, Healing, and Creating

If you are more of a fix-it person, you may want to attend to city trees that need a solid regimen of maintenance. With a little training from an expert and occasional advice from your city forester, you can learn how to help prune and maintain young trees. Some cities are faced with a specific problem or disease— the gypsy moth, oak wilt, or Dutch elm disease—that needs to be addressed and treated. This is the province of local government, but the watchful eyes and concerned voices of citizens are needed as well. Calling attention to trees in trouble can serve to mobilize the community to focus public awareness on other urban forest issues, big and small.

You may choose to establish a wide-ranging plan for your entire community, possibly with a goal toward setting up a separate forestry department if one does not exist. Many projects are begging to be tackled in the urban forest—take your pick. You are limited only by your imagination and energy.

② LIGHTING THE FLAME

Enthusiasm is contagious. If the project is local, you need to identify those who most need to be involved in it. In a street of single-family homes, you could approach your neighbors to find a core group of volunteers. You will probably find that explaining the practical value of trees—both in terms of real estate dollars and the energy savings that trees provide, plus the benefits of beautification of your neighborhood—will be persuasive. Then you can go on to explain some of the global implications involved, even for a small neighborhood project.

Make a special effort to include children from the outset; "kid energy" is a powerful ingredient in the alchemy of community action. Recruiting youngsters is also a fine way to involve their parents and teachers, too. Find the opportunity to address local scout groups; offer your expertise to a teacher or principal of your neighborhood school and volunteer to talk to the students about tree planting in your community; approach your children's soccer, baseball, or hockey team.

If you already belong to a community group, social or business club, charitable organization, or parent-teacher association, you have a built-in audience. Otherwise, try networking at parties and at work. With this book in hand for reference, you could even go door to door. Although not everyone will be receptive to the idea, you will be educating each person you meet about the goals of Global ReLeaf in the best way possible: one-on-one with face-to-face contact. Raising awareness is always the first step to community action.

③ GETTING THE WORD OUT

You can use a variety of publicity outlets to make sure that as many people as possible know about your project. Flyers help, especially when you or one of your volunteers knocks on the door to hand it to someone. Community bulletin boards are important too, but in keeping with the personal approach, try to reach as many people as possible with live presentations: school groups, neighborhood associations, and scout groups are all effective places to educate people and recruit volunteers for the opening day of your tree-planting project. The American Forestry Association publishes quotable information in its *Urban Forests* and *American Forests* magazines and in various Global ReLeaf publications. You can use this information to interest a reporter in a story about trees or to give a presentation at a community meeting.

Be sure to inform the local media: newspapers and radio and television stations. One of the major goals of Global ReLeaf is to educate the public about the benefits of the urban forest, and your group's tree-planting or tree-caring program or activity is proof that the community is really concerned about the state of your city's trees—and they are doing something about it.

The more people who realize the link between the health of the urban forest, tree planting, and the development of a sense of community pride, the easier it will be for your next project—and for the well-being of the urban forest. Attracting media will certainly be easier if you can make a real event out of your tree planting. Combine it with some entertainment, games for children, or a picnic. Tree planting should be recognized for the fun—and environmentally significant activity—that it is.

④ CHOOSING YOUR CORE GROUP

Every operation needs an action team—a core of concerned individuals who will be involved every step of the way. At best, every member of the team should have a different "specialty" and be prepared to see the project through to completion.

The ideal team consists of seven to ten people and includes a lawyer; a technical expert (such as a professional tree person), a volunteer coordinator, a reporter or writer, an engineer, a well-connected business person, and someone from the town, city, or county council. With a team like that and access to major funders, you are ready to play in the big leagues, changing and rewriting regulations. With assured exposure through major media outlets, you will be able to set up programs that will be long-lived and supported by an official network.

For your first project, more than likely you will be happy to settle for a handful of committed individuals whom you can trust to show up when they are needed. Keep a list of everyone who expressed an interest during your initial canvassing, whether for planting or organizing at any level.

⑤ LEARNING THE ROPES AND GETTING THE PERMITS

Chances are you may know very little about how your town or city works. Even if all you want to do is plant a few trees on your street, you will need to know who is responsible and who can give you the green light. Who's in charge? Is it the board of public works, or does your city or town have a separate forestry department? Are park trees under a different jurisdiction than street trees? Ask your city forester to talk to your group about the area's trees and the community's existing tree program. Start communicating with the people who can help you.

What are the steps needed to get permission for your project? Do you know an elected official who is prepared to help? Your public library will probably carry a public officials roster with the list you are looking for. The more homework you do, the more responsive you will find city officials to be, easing the whole process. And the expertise you gain at this stage will prepare you for the challenges ahead.

Friends of Trees

In recent years, it has become increasingly clear that our urban forests could use friend or two; and Portland, Oregon, has found exactly that in Friends of Trees. Led by founder and executive director Richard Seidman, Friends of Trees has mobilized area citizens in planting and caring for trees, predominantly in inner-city neighborhoods.

Seidman decided to start a local tree-planting operation after reading an article about Global ReLeaf in the *Christian Science Monitor* in 1988. But all Seidman had was an idea. He had no funding, no staff, and no models, since Portland was not yet home to any urban forestry groups. But the potential devastation caused by global warming and the desire to involve citizens in improving the environment propelled Seidman to quit his job as a teacher and start building what has become a successful tree-planting organization.

Over the last two years, Friends of Trees has mobilized Portland's neighborhood groups, businesses, and government agencies to implement large-scale tree-planting projects amounting to 600 street trees and 2,700 seedlings in the ground.

To delegate the work and create a sense of community, Friends of Trees works with ten neighborhood groups by providing financial contributions, technical assistance, and moral support. One volunteer from Friends of Trees is assigned to work with each of the neighborhood groups, monitoring the health of the trees after they are planted, which is an important part of the organization's philosophy. Before any group receives support from Friends of Trees, it must show a commitment to long-term tree maintenance.

In the fall of 1989, as the result of a matching grant from E & J Gallo Winery, Friends of Trees launched a major education campaign describing the global challenges of deforestation and global warming and promoting the benefits of urban trees. As part of the campaign, they worked with the Oregon Association of Nurserymen to provide discounts on trees purchased by individuals and neighborhood groups.

You may need a permit, a step that will ensure that you will be planting the proper tree for the site you have chosen. Develop a good working relationship with a particular individual at the agency involved. It is this person's job to work with you, not against you, so learn to cooperate with him or her, and make sure to let the person know you appreciate the help. Keep everyone at the agency or agencies abreast of all developments in your project. Surprises are generally unwelcome arrivals at local bureaucracies. And if you run up against official opposition, learn what changes you will have to make before they say "yes."

⑥ ROUNDING UP SUPPORT

Projects on public property can cost a lot of money. Remember, planting the tree is only the beginning of the process. The American Forestry Association estimates that planting and caring for a street tree for the first five years of its life costs about $300, including $60 for the cost of the tree. About a third of the total cost is for general maintenance after the first year. Ideally, about $100 of that is placed in a trust fund for the tree at the time of planting. Hopefully, raising the money will not be too difficult. The places to look for the green stuff are limited only by your imagination.

Local sources. Start your campaign for funds close to home. The most immediate sources are local businesses, homeowners' associations, local Kiwanis and Rotary clubs, and the chamber of commerce. You might even organize a neighborhood yard sale, bake sale, or car wash to drum up more support, as well as funds, in your community.

If the trees are on a main thoroughfare, you may be able to get individual merchants to contribute the money for trees in front of their property. Make sure you explain how the trees will upgrade the neighborhood and increase foot traffic. Other local establishments may donate money if the planting is done as a block-improvement project. Some local businesses may gladly make service or product contributions when the project is designed to attract public attention. A printer or copy shop may do flyers and letters for free; a restaurant or dairy may provide snacks for the planting event; a hardware store might supply you with tools; a nursery could provide equipment, soil amendments, or even some of the trees at a discount. Just be sure their participation is recognized publicly, and don't be surprised if you find a handful of enthusiastic merchants joining in and planting trees along with you. Remember that the residents of any neighborhood also represent the companies and organizations they work for, and they may be willing to sponsor the projects in their "front yard."

Corporations. A 1990 Roper poll found that 80 percent of Americans consider themselves environmentalists and use their purchasing power to support environmentally sensitive companies. Global ReLeaf has found a wide range of corporate interest and support, from that of oil and financial companies to

food and tree-care companies. Many corporations, from Dayton-Hudson, a major Midwest department-store chain; to the Aveda Corporation, an environmentally sensitive manufacturer of salon-distributed hair and skin products, are involved in supporting Global ReLeaf.

Designing the project to enhance corporate support is very important. Texaco has supported Global ReLeaf, not only through financial underwriting of quality projects proposed by local groups, but also through Texaco people-power. Texaco employees have received training to participate in tree-planting and tree-care projects, and it is hoped that they will continue to be a part of the conservation movement in their communities. The Discovery Channel, a major cable network with nature and environmental programming, supports Global ReLeaf in many ways, including on-air public service announcements and through their cable company affiliates' involvement in local tree-planting projects. Discovery has also assisted by producing a television special called "In Celebration of Trees," which aired in December 1991.

Utilities. Utility companies, in particular, have made a special commitment to energy conservation and are recognizing the value of trees in this effort. The Edison Electric Institute, whose member companies produce 75 percent of the country's electric power, has set a goal to be a major sponsor of Global ReLeaf as part of its customer education, community, and public relations programs. You may also find that your local gas, water, or telephone company is willing to provide the equipment and operators to help you dig through some of the cinder-block-hard city soil so often found in playgrounds and under sidewalks.

Developers. Local developers with projects in the works may well want to participate in an environmental improvement project that benefits the community where their project is located. Try approaching developers before they begin building. Sometimes local ordinances concerning lot lines, house plans, or other technical issues may require builders to remove more trees than they would like. At this point, they can use your support. Global ReLeaf for New Communities, co-sponsored by the American Forestry Association and the National Association of Home

Builders (the trade association for the building industry), recognizes and promotes exemplary developments that save existing trees and plant new ones. With about 800,000 acres of land developed each year, the opportunity for expanding our urban forest and creating a good environment for trees to grow in the future is significant.

⑦ MAKING IT HAPPEN

With luck and perseverance, your local government will give the go-ahead for a full-fledged community tree program. If they don't, continue to develop a constituency for one and approach them next year. Alternatively, you may find private or corporate funding to defray the full costs of your proposed program. Once the funds have been established for a tree program, the local government will hire an urban forester and the first part of your task is completed. Congratulations! All that remains now is your continued involvement in developing strong ties between your core group, the community, the forester, and the local government—plus planting and caring for the trees, of course.

⑧ BECOMING TREE STEWARDS

The least glamorous but most necessary part of community tree planting comes after the ground has been prepared and the tree lovingly planted. Remember: If you are planting a tree on a busy city street in a central part of the city, you are choosing a concrete jungle for its new home. The young tree will need constant care in its early years, and regular maintenance after that. Even in relatively hospitable areas of the city, young trees still need a regular schedule of watering, care, and inspection. Depending on the species and the weather conditions, the young trees may need special care for the first three to five years. And after the first year or so, they need to be inspected by a person trained to identify damage by pests and disease. By the third year, your young trees will need corrective pruning to remove dead and damaged branches as well as those growing in a direction that will cause problems later in life. These branches should be snipped by a trained pruner with a steady hand. Assuming that the city has not taken over the task, citizen volunteers can be trained to assist with the job. And then, for the rest of the tree's life, someone needs to make sure that the tree you worked so hard to plant achieves its full promise and maximum benefit as part of the urban forest. Global ReLeaf, after all, puts its emphasis on the volume of leaves that branch out into our cities, not the number of bare stems in the ground.

EDUCATING THE CHILDREN

Planting and caring for trees is only part of the Global ReLeaf process. Planting ideas and hope in the minds of children is just as important. Teachers across the country have found that children love to discover the wonders and mysteries of the urban forest close at hand. Some schools may take part in an actual planting; others may go on a field trip, surveying streets for the kinds of trees and animals in the urban forest; still others can be exposed to the most important concepts through entertaining presentations and slide shows.

Several local tree-planting organizations have developed

curriculum material that use the study of the urban forest as a springboard to a wealth of other environmentally related issues and subjects. The "Global ReLeaf Curriculum Guide" contains five lesson plans to teach fourth to sixth graders about the environmental value of trees and forests and includes information on conducting a tree survey and planting trees (see Resources section). Projects may vary from area to area, but here are a few ideas for hands-on activities that children everywhere will enjoy:

🍂 **Getting to know the trees of the neighborhood.** Local field trips will help children learn the most basic elements of the urban forest: the difference between conifers and deciduous trees, for instance. Younger children can count the number of trees on their way to school and develop a tree map of the area. Older children can learn the names of the varieties that grow in their area and something about their natural history.

🍂 **Tree journals.** Each child can keep a journal on a particular tree. They can draw it during different seasons of the year, collect

samples of bark, leaves, and seeds, and observe the kinds of wildlife—from ants to squirrels and birds—that they see and study.

Leaf activities. Children can carry out a number of art projects with leaves, including making leaf prints, collages, and rubbings. They can also catalog a leaf collection, or make a leaf press.

Germinating a tree from a seed. Perhaps one of the seeds collected from a local species gathered on a class outing could be germinated at home or in the classroom. Transplanting a seedling that has sprouted and is growing out of place in a garden or flower bed could be another project.

Making mulch. Here is a great opportunity to delve into the life cycles of trees: How dead material is recycled back into the earth; how carbon dioxide, oxygen, and water are recycled through the composted leaves. Lots of lessons here!

🍂 **The anatomy of a tree.** Older children can be introduced to the detailed structure and function of the parts of a tree and how a tree's processes are influenced by living in the city as opposed to the forest. Roots, leaves, xylem, phloem, and bark can all be examined under a microscope.

🍂 **Global warming.** Build a simple "greenhouse" from used windows or panes of glass, and explain how a similar process is at work in our atmosphere.

🍂 **A walk on the wild side.** Visit a rural forest, preferably for longer than a day, to discover the joys of nature. This is a perfect time for children to discover a natural ecosystem and the cycles within it. Back in the city, students can compare the rural and the urban forest. They may be surprised to find that, despite their differences, the two function in similar ways.

🍂 **Recycling.** Start a recycling program in the classroom and encourage children to institute one at home, too. This may also be a way for children to earn a little extra money—maybe for tree planting! In high schools with large student populations, thorough recycling can result in hundreds of dollars a month for student projects or tree care.

GLOBAL RELEAF COMES FULL CIRCLE

Global ReLeaf is a call to action. Human beings have created serious environmental problems that we all need to address. We face significant environmental challenges on a global scale, as well as around our homes, in our communities, on our farms, and in our forests. In this book, we've offered the chance to get started on the solutions. Your part can be as straightforward as planting a tree around your own home or as involved as organizing community action and joining with other groups worldwide through the Global ReLeaf network. By planting just one tree properly, you can learn a valuable lesson about ecology—one that will help you see and be part of the environment in a new way. This first step can lead to an important, and enjoyable, commitment to personal action for environmental improvement.

Natural Resources

We hope this book has stimulated your interest in the urban forest and provided you with some useful ideas about how you might become more involved in it. The organizations, materials, and companies listed in this section may be of further help in turning these ideas into reality.

NATIONAL TRADE, PROFESSIONAL, AND CITIZEN ORGANIZATIONS

American Association of Botanical Gardens and Arboreta, 786 Church Road, Wayne, PA 19087; (215) 688-1120.

American Association of Nurserymen (AAN), 1250 I St., N.W., Suite 500, Washington, DC 20005; (202) 789-2900. Contact them to obtain a list of garden centers and wholesale nurseries in your region.

American Forestry Association (AFA), P.O. Box 2000, Washington, DC 20013; (202) 667-3300; FAX (202) 667-7751. The nation's oldest citizen conservation organization for trees and forests.

American Society of Landscape Architects, 4401 Connecticut Ave., N.W., Washington, DC 20008; (202) 686-ASLA. Call for references and listings for large-scale planting projects by individuals or community groups.

Edison Electric Institute, 701 Pennsylvania Ave., N.W., Suite 400, Washington, DC 20004; (202) 508-5000.

International Society of Arboriculture (ISA), P.O. Box 908, Urbana, IL 61801; (217) 328-2032. Call for a catalog of available materials and a list of arborist members in your region.

National Arborist Association (NAA), National Headquarters, P.O. Box 1094, Amherst, NH 03031-1094; (603) 673-3311. Check your telephone book for your local chapter, or contact the national headquarters for a list of members in your area.

National Arbor Day Foundation, 211 N. 12th St., Lincoln, NE 68508; (402) 474-5655. Sponsors of "Tree City USA."
National Association of State Foresters, 444 N. Capital St., N.W., Suite 526, Washington, DC 20001; (202) 624-5415.
National Tree Trust, 1455 Pennsylvania Ave., N.W., Suite 250, Washington, DC 20004; (202) 628-TREE.
National Weather Service, General Information; (301) 713-0622. To find out the direction of prevailing winds and annual rainfall in your area.
Society of American Foresters, 5400 Grosvenor Lane, Bethesda, MD 20814; (301) 897-8720.

FEDERAL AGENCIES

U.S. Department of Agriculture (USDA), Forest Service, Urban and Community Forestry, 210 14th St., S.W., Washington, DC 20250; (202) 205-9694. **Extension Service,** 14th St. and Independence Ave., S.W., Washington, DC 20250; (202) 447-2791.
Soil Conservation Service, Department of Agriculture, Public Information Division, P.O. Box 2890, Washington, DC 20013.
U.S. Department of the Interior, National Park Service, 1849 C St., N.W., Washington, DC 20240; (202) 208-7520. **Bureau of Land Management,** 1849 C St., N.W., Washington, DC 20240; (202) 208-7701.
Environmental Protection Agency (EPA), 401 M St., S.W., Suite 1200-W, Washington, DC 20460; (202) 382-2090.
Council on Environmental Quality, Office of the President, Washington, DC 20503; (202) 395-5750.

EDUCATIONAL MATERIALS

Famous and Historic Trees, P.O. Box 7040, Jacksonville, FL 32238-7040; 1-800-677-0727. Several programs are available, from a single tree to entire groves and forests.
"Global ReLeaf Citizen Action Guide," American Forestry Association, Washington, DC. ($1.50)
"Global ReLeaf Curriculum Guide," American Forestry Association, Washington, DC. Five lesson plans for learning about trees and the environment. ($5)

The Man Who Planted Trees. This poignant, true story for both adults and children was made into an Academy Award–winning animated film. The video version is available for $33.45 postpaid from: CBC Home Video, P.O. Box 6440, Station A, Montreal, Quebec H3C 3L4, Canada; (514) 597-4040.

Save Our Urban Trees, American Forestry Association, Washington, DC. ($7.50)

State, local, or university arboretum. Public and university arboretums often publish guides to local trees, provide tours, and may be able to answer many of your questions about tree-planting in your area.

TreePeople, 12601 Mulholland Drive, Beverly Hills, CA 90210; (310) 273-8733. Publishes a curriculum guide, educational videos, and other materials.

Tree-planting Handbook: A Guide for Organizing Neighborhood Tree-planting Projects, San Francisco Friends of the Urban Forest, 512 Second St., San Francisco, CA 94107; (415) 543-5000.

University or college forestry department. Your nearby institu-tion of higher education may be a valuable resource for informa-tion, educational materials, and professional expertise.

FURTHER READING

American Forests magazine, American Forestry Association, Washington, DC.

Arboriculture: Care of Trees, Shrubs and Vines in the Landscape, Richard W. Harris, Prentice Hall, 1983.

Concepts of Ecology, Edward J. Kormondy, Prentice Hall, 1984.

Creative Home Landscaping, Michael A. Dirr, Ortho Publishing, 1987.

The Forest and the Trees: A Guide to Excellent Forestry, Gordon Robinson, Island Press, 1988.

Forest Farming, J. Holto Douglas & Robert A. Hart. ITDG/NA, 777 U.N. Plaza, Suite 9A, New York, NY 10017; (212) 972-9877.

Global Warming: Are We Entering the Greenhouse Century? Stephen Schneider, Sierra Club Books, 1989.

The Granite Garden: Urban Nature and Human Design, Anne Whiston Spirn, Basic Books, 1984.

Heaven Is Under Our Feet, Don Henley, Longmeadow Press, 1991.

Home Landscape: The Art of Home Landscaping, Garrett Eckbo (enlarged and revised edition), McGraw-Hill, 1978.

How to Plan and Plant Your Own Property, Alice R. Ireys, 1975.

How to Plan Your Own Home Landscape, Nelva M. Weber, Bobbs-Merrill, 1976.

Hugh Johnson's Encyclopedia of Trees, Gallery Books, 1984 (out of print).

Landscaping for Wildlife, Carrol L. Henderson, 1987. Minnesota Bookstore, Documents Division, 117 University Ave., St. Paul, MN 55155; (612) 297-3000.

Landscaping Illustrated, Sunset Books, Lane Publishing, 1978.

Let It Rot: Gardener's Guide to Composting, Stu Campbell, Storey Publishers, 1990.

The Man Who Planted Trees, Jean Giono, Chelsea Green, 1985.

Shading Our Cities: A Resource Guide for Urban and Community Forests, Gary Moll and Sara Ebenreck (eds.), Island Press, 1989.

The Simple Act of Planting a Tree, TreePeople with Andy and Katie Lipkis, Jeremy Tarcher, 1990.

Trees and Shrubs for Dry California Landscapes, Bob Perry, Land Design Publications, 1981.

Trees in Urban Design, Henry F. Arnold, Van Nostrand Reinhold, 1980.

Urban Forestry, Gene Grey and Frederick Deneke, John Wiley and Sons, 1986.

Urban Forestry: Planning and Managing Urban Greenscapes, Robert W. Miller, Prentice Hall, 1988.

Urban Forests magazine, American Forestry Association, Washington, DC.

The Woodland Steward, Jim Fazio, Woodland Press, 1985.

CATALOGS AND MAIL-ORDER SUPPLIERS

If you are only purchasing a few trees, your local nursery may be the best place to buy. Make sure to ask if the nursery adheres to the American Association of Nurserymen (AAN) standards. You may also choose to buy your trees by mail order, especially for harder-to-find species. Here is a guide to some sources:

American Standard for Nursery Stock, American Association of Nurserymen (address on page 108), ($12.50). Helpful when buying in quantity. Although highly technical, this booklet will allow you to make sure that your stock is professionally acceptable.

The Complete Guide to Gardening by Mail, c/o Mail Order Association of Nurseries, 8683 Doves Fly Way, Laurel, MD 20723; (301) 490-9143. (Send $1 for postage and handling.) This guide lists some of the hundreds of catalogs available.

STATE GLOBAL RELEAF COORDINATORS

State Global ReLeaf Coordinators usually work for a state's division of forestry. They are a valuable resource and can provide names of local tree-planting groups.

Alabama: Neil Letson, Alabama Forestry Commission, 513 Madison Ave., Montgomery, AL 36130; (205) 240-9360.
Alaska: Al Hendricks, Alaska Division of Forestry, 400 Willoughbury Ave., Juneau, AK 99801; (907) 561-2020.
Arizona: Joanne Cameroon, Arizona State Land Department, Forestry, 1616 W. Adams, Phoenix, AZ 85007; (602) 542-6191.
Arkansas: Jim Northum, Arkansas Forestry Commission, 3821 W. Roosevelt Road, Little Rock, AR 72214; (501) 664-2531.
California: Jim Geiger, California Department of Forestry and Fire, 1416 9th St., 15th Floor, Sacramento, CA 95814; (916) 322-0109; and Genni Cross, Trust for Public Lands, California ReLeaf, 116 New Montgomery, 3rd Floor, San Francisco, CA 94105; (415) 495-5660.

Colorado: Ron Gosnell, Colorado State Forestry Service, 936 Left Hand Canyon, Boulder, CO 80302; (303) 442-0428.

Connecticut: Bob Ricard, University of Connecticut, Middlesex Extension 1066, Saybrook Road, Haddam, CT 06438; (203) 345-4511; and Fred Borman, DEP–State Office Building, Room 260, 165 Capital Ave., Hartford, CT 06106; (203) 566-5348.

Delaware: David Woodward, Delaware State College, Cooperative Extension, Townsend Hall, Newark, DE 19717; (302) 736-4811; and Duane Green, Department of Agriculture–Forestry, 2320 S. Dupont Highway, Dover, DE 19901; (302) 736-4811.

Florida: Jim Harrell, Department of Agriculture & Consumer Services, Forestry, 3125 Conner Blvd., Tallahassee, FL 32399; (904) 488-5168.

Georgia: Sharon Dolliver, Georgia Forestry Commission, P.O. Box 819, Macon, GA 31298; (912) 744-3377.

Hawaii: Teresa Trueman-Madriaga, Division of Forestry & Wildlife, 1151 Punchbowl St., Honolulu, HI 96813; (808) 548-8850.

Idaho: Mike Brady, Idaho Department of Lands, P.O. Box 670, Coeur d'Alene, ID 83814; (208) 664-2171.

Illinois: Reinee Hildebrandt, Illinois Department of Conservation, 600 N. Grand Ave., West Springfield, IL 62706; (217) 782-2361.

Indiana: John Parry, Indiana Department of Natural Resources, 408 S. 9th St., Suite 207, Noblesville, IN 46060; (317) 773-3089.

Iowa: John Walkowiak, Iowa Department of Natural Resources, Wallace State Office Building, Des Moines, IA 50319; (515) 242-5966.

Kansas: Jim Nighswonger, Department of Forestry, 2610 Claflin Road, Manhattan, KS 66502; (913) 537-7050.

Kentucky: Tim Sheehan, Kentucky Division of Forestry, 627 Comanche Trail, Frankfort, KY 40601; (502) 564-4496.

Louisiana: Bonnie Steine, Department of Agriculture & Forestry, P.O. Box 1628, Baton Rouge, LA 70821; (504) 925-4500.

Maine: Beth Reed, Maine Forest Service, Station 22, Augusta, ME 04333; (207) 289-2791.

Maryland: Gene Piotrowski, Maryland Forest, Park, & Wildlife, 580 Taylor Ave., B2, Annapolis, MD 21401; (301) 974-3776.

Massachusetts: Ernie DeRosa, Department of Environmental Management, 100 Cambridge St., 19th Floor, Boston, MA 02202; (617) 598-1974; and Mass ReLeaf, 100 Cambridge St., 20th Floor, Boston, MA 02202; (617) 727-9800, ext. 273.

Michigan: Melinda Jones, Global ReLeaf of Michigan, 14081 Warner Court, Livonia, MI 48154; (313) 761-4102; and Gordon Terry, Michigan Department of Natural Resources, 530 W. Allegan, Lansing, MI 48933 (517) 373-1275.

Minnesota: Jonathan Stiegler, Minnesota Department of Natural Resources, Box 44, Division of Forestry, St. Paul, MN 55155; (612) 297-3507.

Mississippi: Darlene Slater, Mississippi Forestry Commission, 301 Bldg. North Lamar, Ste. 300, Jackson, MS 39201; (601) 359-1386.

Missouri: James Rocca, Missouri Department of Conservation, P.O. Box 180, Jefferson City, MO 65102; (314) 751-4115.

Montana: Mark Duntemann, Department of State Lands, 2705 Spurgin Road, Missoula, MT 59801; (406) 542-4300.

Nebraska: Dave Mooter, Nebraska Forest Service, 8015 W. Center Road, Omaha, NE 68124; (402) 444-7804.

Nevada: Rich Harvey, Nevada Division of Forestry, 123 W. Nye Lane, Carson City, NV 89710; (702) 687-4350.

New Hampshire: J.B. Cullen, Division of Forests and Lands, 172 Pembroke St., Concord, NH 03302; (603) 271-2214.

New Jersey: Mike D'Errico, Bureau of Forestry Management, New Jersey Forest Service, CN-404, Trenton, NJ 08625; (609) 292-2532.

New Mexico: Jim Freeman, Department of Natural Resources, P.O. Box 1948, Santa Fe, NM 87504; (505) 827-5842.

New York: Pete Innes, Department of Environmental Conservation, Room 406, 50 Wolf Road, Albany, NY 12233; (518) 457-7370; and Nancy Wolf, Environmental Action Coalition, 625 Broadway, New York, NY 10012; (212) 677-1601.

North Carolina: Ginny Russell, Department of Natural Resources, Division of Forest Resources, P.O. Box 27687, Raleigh, NC 27611; (919) 733-2162.

North Dakota: Walter Pasicznyk, North Dakota Forest Service, First and Brander, Bottineau, ND 58318; (701) 228-2277.

Ohio: Drew Todd, Ohio Department of Natural Resources, Division of Forestry, Fountain Square, Columbus, OH 43224; (614) 265-6707.

Oklahoma: Gina Childs, Department of Agriculture, Forestry Division, 2800 N. Lincoln Blvd., Oklahoma City, OK 73105; (405) 521-3864.

Oregon: Paul Ries, Oregon Department of Forestry, 2600 State St., Salem, OR 97310; (503) 373-7854.

Pennsylvania: Norman LaCasse, Department of Environmental Resources–Forestry (FAS), P.O. Box 1467, Harrisburg, PA 17120; (717) 787-5359.

Puerto Rico: Roberto Velez, Department of Natural Resources, P.O. Box 5887, San Juan, PR 00906; (809) 724-3584.

Rhode Island: Bruce Payton, Division of Forest Environment, 1037 Hartford Pike, North Scituate, RI 02857; (401) 647-3367.

South Carolina: Debbie Price, South Carolina Forestry Commission, P.O. Box 21707, Columbia, SC 29221; (803) 737-8800.

South Dakota: Craig Brown, South Dakota Division of Forestry, Sigurd Anderson Building, Pierre, SD 57501; (605) 866-6806.

Tennessee: Bruce Webster, Department of Conservation, Division of Forestry, 701 Broadway, Nashville, TN 37203; (615) 742-6635.

Texas: Don Mueller, Texas Forest Service, 100 Research Parkway, College Station, TX 77843; (409) 845-2641.

Utah: Tony Dietz, Division of State Lands and Forests, 355 West N. Temple, Suite 400, Salt Lake City, UT 84180; (801) 538-5508.

Vermont: Steve Sinclair, Agency of Environmental Conservation, 103 S. Main St., 10 South Waterbury, VT 05676; (802) 244-8716.

Virgin Islands: Eric Bough, Economic Development and Agriculture, King Field Post Office, St. Croix, VI 00820; (809) 778-0997.

Virginia: Bettina Ring, Department of Forestry, P.O. Box 3758, Charlottesville, VA 22903; (804) 977-6555.

Washington: Shelley Farber, Washington Department of Natural Resources–Conservation, 234 E. 8th Ave., EG-11, Olympia, WA 98504; (206) 753-2400.

West Virginia: Bob Whipkey, Department of Natural Resources–Forestry, State Office Building, No. 3, 1800 Washington St., East Charlestown, WV 25305; (304) 348-2788.

Wisconsin: Richard Rideout, Wisconsin Department of Natural Resources, Bureau of Forestry, Box 7921, Madison, WI 53707; (608) 267-0843.

Wyoming: Daniel J. Perko, Wyoming State Forestry Division, 1100 W. 22nd St., Cheyenne, WY 82002; (307) 777-7586.

INTERNATIONAL GLOBAL RELEAF PARTNERS

AUSTRIA: Osterreichischer Naturschutzbund, Haus der Natur Schloss Arenberg, Arenbergstrasse 10, A-5020 Salzburg, Austria; (43) 662-642909; FAX (43) 662-643734.

CANADA: Friends Of The Earth/Global ReLeaf, 251 Laurier Ave., W., Ste. 701, Ottawa, ON, K1P 5J6, Canada; (613) 230-3352; FAX (613) 232-4354.

CZECHOSLOVAKIA: Slovak Union of Nature and Landprotectors, Krizovatka 10, 969 01 Banska Stiavnica SNP 13, Czechoslovakia; (42) 859-21817; (42) 859-23334.

ECUADOR: Fundación Natura, Av. America 5653, Y VOZ Andes, Quito, Ecuador; phone 447-341; FAX 43-44-49.

GERMANY: PRIMA KLIMA, Fichteweg 22, D-4020 Mettmann, Germany; (49) 2104-53362; FAX (49) 2104-51192.

HUNGARY: Independent Ecological Center, Miklositer 1, 1035 Budapest, Hungary; (361) 168-6229; FAX (361) 168-8002.

KENYA: ANEN, P.O. Box 53844, Nairobi, Kenya; phone 28138.

SPAIN: DEPANA, Arago 281 2n2a, 08009, Barcelona, Spain; (343) 215-1484; (343) 487-1560.

UKRAINE: Nat'l Ecological Centre of Ukraine, 252030 Kiev, Volodymirska 54, Ukraine; (044) 221-6592; FAX (044) 266-7104.

UNITED KINGDOM: Global ReLeaf Coordinator, 7 Glengyle Terrace, Edinburgh EH3 9LL, Scotland, United Kingdom.

LOCAL TREE-PLANTING GROUPS

Local tree-planting groups are independent nonprofit partners active under the Global ReLeaf banner.

—ALABAMA—

Athens: Athens-Lime-stone Clean Community, P.O. Box 1089, Athens, AL 35611; (205) 233-8728.

Mobile: Streetscapes, Inc., 70 Croydon Road, Mobile, AL 36608; (205) 342-6133.

—ARIZONA —

Bisbee: Cochise Global ReLeaf, P.O. Box 1496, Bisbee, AZ 85603; (602) 432-9455.

Flagstaff: Flagstaff Clean and Beautiful, 211 W. Aspen, Flagstaff, AZ 86001; (602) 774-5281.

Globe: Copper Cities Global ReLeaf, P.O.Box 687, Globe, AZ 85502; (602) 425-6232.

Gold Canyon: Green the Gold Canyon/A.D.O.B.E., 10880 Cordova Ave., Gold Canyon, AZ 85219; (602) 983-0837.

Oracle: Oracle Global ReLeaf, P.O. Box 700, Oracle, AZ 85623; (602) 896-2425.

Phoenix: Forestry for Phoenix, P.O. Box 3617, Phoenix, AZ 85018; (602) 534-5323.

Prescott: Keep Prescott Beautiful, P.O. Box 2059, Prescott, AZ 86302; (602) 445-3500.

Tucson: Tucson Clean and Beautiful, P.O. Box 27210, Tucson, AZ 85726; (602) 791-3109.

—CALIFORNIA—

Beverly Hills: TreePeople, 12601 Mulholland Drive, Beverly Hills, CA 90210; (310) 273-8733.

Clovis: Tree Fresno, 456 Clovis Ave., Suite 4, Clovis, CA 93612; (209) 323-TREE.

El Segundo: Tree Musketeers, 406 Virginia, El Segundo, CA 90245; (310) 322-0263.

Fresno: Tree Fresno, P.O. Box 4683, Fresno, CA 93744.

Fullerton: Tree Society of Orange County, c/o Fullerton Arboretum, CSUF, Fullerton, CA 92634.

Hermosa Beach: Hermosa ReLeaf, 2966 La Carlita Place, Hermosa Beach, CA 90254; (310) 376-4358.

Los Angeles: Green Islands, 1963 Stearns Drive, Los Angeles, CA 90034; (213) 939-3296; and North East Trees, 4701 Olson St., Los Angeles, CA 90041; (213) 255-4863.

Montebello: TreeMendUs, 636 S. 5th St., Montebello, CA 90640; (213) 722-8278.

Napa: Napa ReLeaf, 2015 Redwood Road, Napa, CA 94558; (707) 255-8413.

Placerville: El Dorado Green Alliance, Box 985, Placerville, CA 95667; and Trees Are Us, 1988 Cold Springs Road, Placerville, CA 95667.

Redlands: Green Leaf, 308 Myrtle St., Redlands, CA 92373.

Richmond: East Bay ReLeaf, 100 37th St., Richmond, CA 94805; (415) 347-3145.

Sacramento: California Oak Foundation, 909 12th St., Suite 100, Sacramento, CA 95814; (916) 929-6400; and Sacramento Tree Foundation, 865 Howe Ave., Sacramento, CA 95825; (916) 924-8733.

San Diego: San Diego People for Trees, City Adminis-tration Building, 202 C St., San Diego, CA 92101; (619) 224-4423.

San Francisco: Friends of the Urban Forest, 512 Second St., 4th Floor, San Francisco, CA 94107; (415) 543-5000.

San Jose: San Jose Beautiful, 138 Stockton, San Jose, CA 95126; (408) 292-9993.

San Rafael: Marin ReLeaf, 72 Brentwood, San Rafael, CA 94901.

Santa Rosa: Sonoma ReLeaf, 620 Lombard Ave., Santa Rosa, CA 95409; (707) 575-0203.

Stanford: Peninsula ReLeaf, P.O. Box 5894, Stanford, CA 94309; (415) 325-2786.

Vandenberg: Vandenberg Air Force Base, 1 STRAD/ET, Building 16109, Vanden-berg, CA 93437-5000; (805) 866-1922.

Walnut Grove: Pacific Coast Tree Foundation, P.O. Box 999, Walnut Grove, CA 95690; (916) 920-4086.

Willits: Willits Friends of the Trees, 216 Redwood Ave., Willits, CA 95490; (707) 459-4567.

—COLORADO—

Buffalo Creek: Trees for Mother Earth, P.O. Box 181, Buffalo Creek, CO 80245; (303) 838-5182.

Denver: Volunteers for Outdoor Colorado, 1410 Grant St., B105, Denver, CO 80203; (303) 830-7792; and Denver Urban Forest, 1700 S. Holly, Denver, CO 80222; (303) 674-2833.

Fort Collins: Plant a Tree, Grow a Friend, 633 S. College, Ft. Collins, CO 80524; (303) 224-2877; and Fort Collins ReLeaf, 633 S. College, Fort Collins, CO 80524; (303) 224-2634.

Pueblo: Trees Please, P.O. Box 4437, Pueblo, CO 81003.

Vail: Vail Valley ReLeaf, Inc., P.O. Box 991, Vail, CO 81658.

—CONNECTICUT—

Hartford: Hartford Trees, 118 Oak St., Hartford, CT 06106; (203) 527-8737.

Norwalk: Norwalk ReLeaf, 102 Ward St., Norwalk, CT 06851.

—DISTRICT OF COLUMBIA—

Washington: Trees for the City, 2013 O St., N.W., Washington, DC 20036; (202) 785-9184.

—FLORIDA—

Bradenton: ReLeaf Manatee, 1115 71st. St., N.W., Bradenton, FL 34209; (813) 794-5840.

Fort Myers: Lee County ReLeaf, P.O. Box 9272, Fort Meyers, FL 33902; (813) 332-7121.

Jacksonville: Green-scapes, P.O. Box 445, Jacksonville, FL 32201; (904) 356-8733; and Jacksonville Botanic Society, P.O. Box 19744, Jacksonville, FL 32245-9744; (904) 642-5013.

Miami: Citizens for a Better South Florida, 2647 S.E. 23rd St., Miami, FL 33145; (305) 444-9555; and Trees for Dade, Florida International University, Miami, FL 33199; (305) 348-3083.

Palm Beach Gardens: TreeFlorida, P.O. Box 31114, Palm Beach Gardens, FL 33420; (407) 622-6966.

Pensacola: Telephone Pioneers, 6915 Pine Forest Road, Pensacola, FL 32526; (904) 436-1655.

Sarasota: ReLeaf Sarasota County, 2620 Grafton St., Sarasota, FL 34231; (813) 922-3693.

—GEORGIA—

Atlanta: Trees Atlanta, 96 Poplar St., N.W., Atlanta, GA 30303; (404) 522-4097.

Columbus: Keep Columbus Beautiful Committee, Box 428, Columbus, GA 31902; (404) 571-4937.

Rome: Garden Club of Georgia, Inc., 2642 Lake Ridge Circle, Rome, GA 30161; (404) 234-2235.

Savannah: Savannah Tree Foundation, 12736 Rockwell Ave., Savannah, GA 31419; (912) 925-7250; and Savannah Area Garden Clubs, 305 E. 52nd St., Savannah, GA 31405; (912) 238-4049.

—HAWAII—

Honolulu: The Nature Conservancy of Hawaii, 1116 Smith St., Suite 201, Honolulu, HI 96817; (808) 537-4508.

119

—ILLINOIS—

Chicago: Open Lands Project, 220 S. State St., Suite 1880, Chicago, IL 60604; (312) 427-4256.

—INDIANA—

Fort Wayne: Hoosier ReLeaf, 4405 W. Washington Center Road, Fort Wayne, IN 46818; (219) 489-4614.

South Bend: Sierra Club, 58712 Crumstown Highway, South Bend, IN 46619; (219) 287-5812.

Terre Haute: TREES, 3500 Hulan St., Terre Haute, IN 47803; (812) 232-4331.

—IOWA—

Cedar Rapids: Trees Forever, 5190 42nd St., N.E., Cedar Rapids, IA 52402; (319) 373-0650.

Des Moines: Iowa Heritage Foundation, 505 Fifth Ave., Suite 444, Des Moines, IA 50309-2315; (515) 288-1846.

—KANSAS—

Kansas City: Trees for Kansas, 1003 Orville Ave., Kansas City, KS 66102; (913) 573-2942.

—KENTUCKY—

Frankfort: Juvenile Services, Office of Courts, 100 Millcreek Parkway, Frankfort, KY 40601; (502) 564-2350.

—LOUISIANA—

Baton Rouge: Baton Rouge Green, 7330 Highland Rd., Suite 123, Baton Rouge, LA 70806; (504) 768-7103.

Covington: Covington Tree Alliance, 95 North Dogwood Drive, Covington, LA 70433; (504) 898-0257.

New Orleans: Audubon Institute, P.O. Box 4327, New Orleans, LA 70718; (504) 861-2537; and Longue Vue House and Gardens, 7 Bamboo Road, New Orleans, LA 70124; (504) 488-5488.

Shreveport: Shreveport Green, 3007 Knight St., Suite 107, Shreveport, LA 71105; (318) 865-6455.

—MAINE—

Old Towne: Maine ReLeaf, P.O. Box 433, Old Towne, ME 04468; 1-800-648-4202.

—MARYLAND—

Annapolis: Annapolis ReLeaf Committee, 915 Creek Drive, Annapolis, MD 21403; (301) 261-2289.

Chevy Chase: Bethesda Ever Green, 33 W. Irving St., Chevy Chase, MD 20815; (301) 468-4940.

Landover: Anacostia Watershed Society, P.O. Box 1309, Landover, MD 20785; (301) 459-9200.

Silver Springs: Trees for the Future, 11306 Estona Dr., Box 1786, Silver Springs, MD 20902; (301) 929-0238.

—MICHIGAN—

Detroit: Greening of Detroit, 600 Renaissance Center, Suite 1400, Detroit, MI 48243; (313) 393-1910.

Grand Rapids: Center for Environmental Studies, 143 Bostwick, N.E., Grand Rapids, MI 49506; (616) 456-4848; Western Michigan Environmental Action Council, 1432 Wealthy, S.E., Grand Rapids, MI 49506; (616) 451-3051; and International Trees Corps, 1900 Wealthy, S.E., Suite 290, Grand Rapids, MI 49506; (616) 774-0191.

Williamsburg: The Chestnut Alliance, P.O. Box 3, Williamsburg, MI 49690; (616) 264-6889.

—MINNESOTA—

St. Lewis Park: Twin Cities Tree Trust, 4100 Vernon Ave. South, St. Lewis Park, MN 55416; (612) 920-9326.

—MISSOURI—

Springfield: Project Parkway, 3016 S. Murphy Road, Springfield, MO 65809; (417) 887-7739.

—NEBRASKA—

Battle Creek: Parks of Pride Foundation, Inc., 101 E. Main St., Battle Creek, NE 68715; (402) 675-8185.

Boys Town: Father Flannigan's Boys Home, Boys Town, NE 69101; (402) 498-3282.

North Platte: Trees for North Platte, Rt. 4, Box 46A, North Platte, NE 69101.

Ogallala: Make Ogallala Beautiful, Inc., 319 E. "A," Box 702, Ogallala, NE 69153; (308) 284-2456.

—NEVADA—

Las Vegas: Growing Solutions, P.O. Box 11242, Las Vegas, NV 89111-1242; (702) 486-5123.

—NEW JERSEY—

Madison: Friends of Madison Shade Trees, Inc., Ardsleigh Drive, Madison, NJ 07940; (201)377-6292.

—NEW MEXICO—

Albuquerque: Indian Pueblo Culture Center, 2410 12th St., N.W., Albuquerque, NM 87102; (505) 843-7270; and Tree New Mexico, Alvarado Square, Albu-querque, NM 87158; (505) 848-4554.

Crownpoint: The Navajo Nation, Crownpt. Agency, P.O. Box 519, Crownpoint, NM 87313; (505) 786-5543.

Taos: Trees for Taos, Rt. 2, Box 127, Taos, NM 87571.

—NEW YORK—

Brooklyn: Prospect Park Alliance, 95 Prospect Park West, Brooklyn, NY 11215-3709; (718) 965-8951.

Gloversville: Gloversville ReLeaf, 32 Spring St., Gloversville, NY 12078; (518) 725-4515.

New York: Street Tree Consortium, 44 Worth St., New York, NY 10013 (212) 227-1887;Green Guerrillas, 625 Broadway, New York, NY 10012; (212) 674-8124; Neighborhood Open Space Coalition, 72 Reade St., New York, NY 10007; (212) 513-7555; and Environmental Action Coalition, 625 Broadway, New York, NY 10012; (212) 677-1601.

Rye: Trees for Rye, c/o Rye Conservation Society, P.O. Box 274, Rye, NY 10580; (914) 967-5150.

—NORTH CAROLINA—

Asheville: Quality Forward, P.O. Box 22, Asheville, NC 28802; (704) 254-1776.

Cashiers: Trail of Trees, P.O. Box 553, Marketbasket Highway 107, Cashiers, NC 28717; (704) 743-2216.

Charlotte: ReLeaf Charlotte, P.O. Box 6155, Charlotte, NC 28207; (704) 334-2015.

Greenville: Releaf, Inc., P.O. Box 4072, Greenville, NC 27836-2072.

—OKLAHOMA—

Oklahoma City: Greater Oklahoma City Tree Bank, 621 N. Robinson, Suite 58, Oklahoma City, OK 73102; (405) 236-2280.

Tulsa: Up With Trees!, Tulsa Garden Center, 2435 S. Peoria, Tulsa, OK 74114; (918) 743-9161.

—OHIO—

Akron: Keep Akron Beautiful, 850 E. Market, Akron, OH 44305; (216) 375-2116.

Columbus: Global ReLeaf of Columbus, 1519 Aberdeen Ave., Columbus, OH 43211; (614) 263-8749.

Lebanon: Clean Warren County, 300 E. Silver St., Lebanon, OH 45036; (513) 933-1185.

Mentor: Holden Arboretum, 9500 Sperry Road, Mentor, OH 44060; (216) 946-4400.

—OREGON—

Portland: Friends of Trees, P.O. Box 49851, Portland, OR 97240; (503) 775-1829.

—PENNSYLVANIA—

Philadelphia: Morris Arboretum, 9414 Meadowbrook Ave., Philadelphia, PA 19118; (215) 247-5777; and Philadelphia Green, 325 Walnut St., Philadelphia, PA 19106; (215) 625-8280.

Plymouth Meeting: TerraVision Foundation, 214 Blue Ridge Road, Plymouth Meeting, PA 19462; (215) 828-8034.

—RHODE ISLAND—

North Kingstown: Street Tree, P.O. Box 456, North Kingstown, RI 02852; (809) 785-9450.

121

—SOUTH CAROLINA—
Charleston: Lowcountry ReLeaf, P.O. Box 1812, Charleston, SC 29402; (803) 723-9470.

—TENNESSEE—
Bristol: Keep Bristol Beautiful, 911 Anderson St., Bristol, TN 37620; (615) 764-2411.

Nashville: Keep Nashville Beautiful, Centennial Park Office, Nashville, TN 37201; (615) 862-8418; and ReLeaf Tennessee, 300 Orlando Ave., Nashville, TN 37209-3200; (615) 353-1133.

—TEXAS—
Austin: TreeFolks, 1710 Eva St., Austin, TX 78704; (512) 447-9706; and Austin ReLeaf, 1000 Westbank Drive, Suite 6A, Austin, TX 78746; (512) 327-9141.

Dallas: Dallas Park Foundation, 400 South Record, 6th Floor, Dallas, TX 75265; (214) 977-6653.

El Paso: Rio Grande ReLeaf, 10228 Stoneway, El Paso, TX 79925; (915) 592-1782.

Houston: Trees For Houston, P.O. Box 13096, Houston, TX 77219; (713) 523-8733.

Midland: Keep Midland Beautiful, 500 N. Lorraine, Suite 191, Midland, TX 79701; (915) 688-4190.

San Antonio: San Antonio Trees, 8331 Fredericksburg Road, Suite 311, San Antonio, TX 78229; (512) 615-0828.

—UTAH—
Salt Lake City: Tree Utah, 736 E. 800 South, Salt Lake City, UT 84102; (801) 363-5900.

—VIRGIN ISLANDS—
St. Croix: St. Croix Environmental Association, H6 Company St., Christiansted, St. Croix, VI 00820; (809) 773-1989.

—VIRGINIA—
Arlington: Arlington ReLeaf, 1706 N. Adams, Arlington, VA 22201; (202) 357-2811.

Bristol: Keep Bristol Beautiful, P.O. Box 519, 20 Volunteer Parkway, Bristol, VA 24201-0519; (615) 968-4399.

Fairfax: Fairfax ReLeaf, P.O. Box 1184, Fairfax, VA 22030; (703) 273-3030.

Herdon: Tree Action, P.O. Box 1306, Herdon, VA 22070; (703) 471-4337.

Roanoke: ReLEAF Roanoke Valley, c/o Chamber of Commerce, 310 First St., Roanoke, VA 24011.

—WASHINGTON—
Seattle: Keep Washington Green Association, Anderson Hall, UW AR-10, Seattle, WA 98195; (206) 543-2750; and Plant Amnesty, 906 N.W. 87th St., Seattle, WA 98117; (206) 783-9813.

—WISCONSIN—
Burlington: Trees for Burlington, 441 Hawthorn St., Burlington, WI 53105; (414) 763-9454.

GLOSSARY

backfill: to return the soil to a planting area from which it was originally dug.

bare-root seedling: a tree ready for transplanting that has had the soil removed from around its roots.

cambium: the thin layer within plants or bark of trees, where new cells are manufactured and new growth comes.

chloroplasts: units of chlorophyll within leaves; plant cells in which photosynthesis takes place.

desertification: a process by which land becomes increasingly unproductive and barren.

drain sump: a pipe that helps to remove excess water from a planting hole.

evapotranspiration: the rate at which plants lose water through a combination of evaporation of surface moisture and transpiration (sweat) through the microscopic stomata on the surface of the leaves.

feeder roots: the system of progressively smaller roots that grow upwards from the major roots of a tree in a complex web that forms a mat or fan, ending in a network of fine fibers.

global warming: overall rise in the temperature of the Earth's atmosphere; a projected result of increased greenhouse effect.

greenhouse effect: warming of the Earth's atmosphere produced by the increase of carbon dioxide and certain other gases in the air, trapping the sun's energy near the surface of the Earth.

greenways (or greenbelts): open spaces planted with grass and other vegetation that surround and/or stretch into cities to provide a visual break within and between built-up urban areas.

heartwood: inner, nonliving layers of wood within a tree's trunk; made from xylem that is no longer functioning.

indicator species: a plant or animal species that is used to determine environmental health or safety.

mycorrhizae: symbiotic fungi that live on tree roots and help the tree obtain nutrients from the soil.

particulate matter: microscopic dust particles in the air.

phloem: the layer of tissue which transports nutrients up and down the trunk of the tree.

photosynthesis: the process by which green plants convert sunlight, water, and carbon dioxide into new plant tissue and oxygen.

rainwater harvesting: technique that diverts rainwater runoff for irrigation purposes.

root ball: the clump of soil containing the roots of a tree, often bound in burlap when purchased from a nursery.

root collar: top of the root ball; point at which roots originate.

rototiller: power-driven machine that uses rotating metal teeth to chop, separate, and mix soil; a necessity for planting more than one or two trees.

sand-set pavers: Bricks or flat stones set into sand around a tree that allow water to penetrate to the roots while protecting them from pedestrian traffic.

sapling: young tree whose trunk measures two to four inches in diameter.

sapwood: see xylem.

seedling: a young tree one to two growing seasons old.

sidewalk pit: small preserves of soil found in urban centers, usually within sidewalks. These pits are often the only place for trees in these areas, and constitute a kind of immovable street planter.

swales: shallow trenches dug out to follow the contour of the land for irrigation purposes.

transport roots: the major woody roots that grow horizontally away from the trunk and support the tree.

tree lawn (grassy boulevard, greenbelt, nature strip, or parkway): the usually narrow area between curb and sidewalk.

tree shelter: surrounding sheath, usually made of polypropylene, used to protect a seedling or small tree.

urban heat island: the phenomenon of higher temperatures in a city compared to the surrounding countryside, caused by the combination of paved surfaces, lack of shade, and heat retention of buildings and other structures.

well-aerated soil: soil that has been loosened enough so that at least 50 percent of its volume is air.

well-developed soil: undisturbed soil, as on the floor of a forest, with many levels: organic matter is at the top, minerals are closer to the bottom.

whip: a young tree; often a bud graft on an established root system that has developed a main stem but very few branches.

Xeriscape™: a water-efficient landscape design characterized by the use of drought-resistant plants and reduced or shaded lawn areas.

xylem: outer living layer of a tree which conducts water up and down the trunk; sapwood.

zeroscape: landscape devoid of vegetation, often composed of crushed rock.

ABOUT THE AUTHORS

Gary Moll is the vice president for urban forestry of the American Forestry Association. He holds a forestry degree from Michigan State University and is a nationally known expert on urban forestry. Moll was the forester for a Midwest electric utility, and his responsibilities included managing the company nursery. He was also the state urban forester for the Maryland Forest Service. He is active in bringing together many professional and citizen groups for the benefit of the urban forest resource. He has served as chairman of the National Urban Forest Council and has been recognized for his national urban forestry efforts by the Society of American Foresters and the International Society of Arboriculture. Moll was one of only six Americans, and the only urban forester, to present a paper at the 1991 World Forestry Congress in Paris. He is the editor of *Urban Forests* magazine, author of numerous articles on urban forestry, and editor of *Shading Our Cities: A Resource Guide for Urban and Community Forests.*

Stanley Young is the author of *The Amazing L.A. Environment: A Handbook for Change, The Missions of California,* and *The Big Picture: The Murals of Los Angeles.* He writes regularly on the environment and a wide range of other subjects for *People* magazine, *Los Angeles Magazine,* and *Whole Earth Review,* among other publications in the United States and Great Britain. Young was a postgraduate Commonwealth Scholar in philosophy at the University of Manchester and holds a master's degree in politics from Durham University in England. He has served as a field officer for CARE at a Cambodian refugee camp on the Thai/Kampuchean border, and worked as a modern dancer, gourmet chef, and hatha-yoga teacher. He now lives and works in Venice, California, with his wife, Janice, and baby daughter, Alyssa Rosalie.

ABOUT THE ILLUSTRATOR

Cartoonist/illustrator **Thomas C. Whittemore** focused on primate behavior while at Harvard. Having missed proper introduction to good humor at the Lampoon Club, he went on a quest to find humor in the human condition, traveling the world as a freighter deckhand, oil doodlebugger, railroad gandy dancer, and bargeman. He finished his studies in physical anthropology with a master's degree from the University of Chicago, and began to seek legitimacy as a cartoonist. With the support of his wife, Michele, he now draws from a unique vantage point in Seattle.

ABOUT GLOBAL RELEAF

Global ReLeaf is an international education and action campaign to increase awareness about positive actions that people can take to help mitigate the root causes of global environmental problems, including the global warming threat. The campaign focuses primarily on the opportunities inherent in improving trees and forests, a topic central to the American Forestry Association's mission and expertise. People can take many actions in this area with little or no technical difficulty or financial strain. It is a timely, achievable environmental proposition.

WAYS TO GET INVOLVED WITH GLOBAL RELEAF

Become a Global ReLeaf Contributing Member. Your tax-deductible contribution of $25 will allow us to reach more people with our message of tree-planting action and fund the planting of trees in towns and cities across America. Send your contribution to the address below.

Call our Action Line to plant a tree. Call 1-900-420-4545 and Global ReLeaf will plant a tree to help rebuild a damaged forest ecosystem. The cost of the call is $5. We will also send you additional information on the Global ReLeaf campaign.

Plant Famous and Historic Trees. The American Forestry Association is growing the progeny of 1,500 of the nation's most famous and historically significant trees. You or your organization can sponsor the planting of special Famous and Historic Tree Groves in your community. Call 1-800-677-0727 for details.

For more information on Global ReLeaf's programs, services, and merchandise, call 1-800-368-5748, or write to:

Global ReLeaf
P.O. Box 2000
Dept. GGC
Washington, DC 20013